Amulets
to
Isotopes

For my wife Bet,
for her total support and encouragement

Amulets
to
Isotopes

A History of Medicine in Caithness

D.H.A. BOYD, MD, FRCP Ed

Foreword by the Rt Hon Robert Maclennan, MP

JOHN DONALD PUBLISHERS LTD
EDINBURGH

ISBN 0 85976 500 8

British Library Cataloguing in Publication Data.

A catalogue record for this book is available
from the British Library.

Typesetting & origination by Brinnoven, Livingston.
Printed & bound in Great Britain by Bookcraft Ltd, Midsomer Norton.

Contents

Acknowledgements

It would be impossible to produce a book of this kind without the unstinted help of many individuals and institutions and it is a pleasure to record my thanks to them. I am particularly grateful to the staff of the National Library of Scotland, including the manuscript and map departments; to the staff of the Scottish Record Office; to the staff of the Library of the Royal College of Physicians of Edinburgh; the Highland Council Archives at Inverness and Wick; the Wick Society, the Information and Statistics Division of the National Health; Northern Service in Scotland; Aberdeen University Library; Health Services Archives at Aberdeen, Inverness and Wick.

Many individuals have given freely of their time in supplying me with information and giving help in various ways. They include Dr Dorothy Lunt of the Glasgow Dental School; Dr Colleen Batey of the Glasgow Art Gallery and Museum; Dr Rosalind Marshall, Scottish National Portrait Gallery; Mr Michael Little, Museum of Antiquities Library, Edinburgh; Dr Caroline Wickham-Jones, Mr R. F. Coghill; Mr. William Garrett; Mr James Miller, Dr Frank Foden; Mr Donald Young; Mr Morris Pottinger; Dr Isobel Alexander; Mrs Stella Roxburgh; Mr Donald Omand; Mr Clive Richards; Mr Iain Sutherland; Miss F. R. Watson; Dr Michael Heasman; Mr Mario Luciani; Mrs Trudi Mann and Mrs Mather; Mr Donald Lamont and Dr W.I. Sircus. I am particularly indebted to Dr Reginald Passmore who read the manuscript and made invaluable comments

Members of the medical, nursing and other health-care professions in Caithness – past and present – have provided much information. Dr P.D. Robertson, in addition, read part of the early manuscript and made helpful and constructive suggestions. Others include Dr James Deans; Dr Jack Sutherland; Dr Elizabeth Finlayson; Dr Ian Burns; Dr James Leask; Miss May Sutherland; Miss Rosalind Stamp; Mr Peter Cowell.

It is also my pleasure to record generous financial support for this book from the Guthrie Trust of the Scottish Society of the History of Medicine and the Carnegie Trust for the Universities of Scotland.

Foreword

by the Rt Hon Robert Maclennan, MP

ILLNESS AND ITS TREATMENT in a particular locality from prehistoric times to the present is a subject which might be thought capable of inducing morbid reflections on the imperfectibility of the human species, particularly when considered in its social setting. But the interest, indeed the underlying excitement, of this study of medical history in Caithness is the evidence which it draws together giving good reason to 'say not the struggle naught availeth'. Progress may be crabwise – earlier palliatives may have offered more comfort than some modern cures – but in this story hope is not always deferred. Milestones are reached and left behind. Superstition gives way to experience. Avoidance of disease by exclusion gives way to a duty of care. Endemic squalor is replaced by public health provision. The seasonal terrors of infectious diseases no longer deplete the classrooms and sadden family life. It is a tale told by a wise man, full of incident and pathos and streaked with noble purpose. It signifies the endless striving of men and women to come to terms with all the ills that flesh is heir to. And like all the best epics it is flecked with wry wit and human comedy. The immediacy of the story springs from its local setting but since it offers such universal encouragement it will be enjoyed far beyond the bounds of Caithness.

Robert Maclennan

Preface

JUST TO THE NORTH-EAST of the coastal village of Lybster, at West Clyth, a minor road runs very straight and almost due north to Camster. There, evidence of some of the earliest settlers in Caithness comes dramatically into view in the form of the Grey Cairns, chambered tombs built about 3800 BC. Continue travelling north and on the road west from Thurso, on the coast facing the Pentland Firth, another human artefact appears. Huge compared to the cairns but equally dramatic, the Dounreay Atomic Energy Establishment symbolises the enormous cultural gap between the people who raised the cairns and the present day inhabitants of the area. The sites are separated by some eighteen miles as the crow flies and the populations are separated by about five and a half thousand years but the enormity of the difference in the ways of life is difficult to imagine.

One of these differences relates to sickness and the way it was regarded and dealt with. Some of the diseases the early settlers suffered would be familiar to us and a broken bone or toothache is the same in any era. The men and women who might be asked to help the sufferer however, would be vastly different in their knowledge, beliefs, training and status in their society. The early concepts of the causes of disease related more to forces of nature and supernatural influences than to the study of scientific facts which we claim as more worthy of attention. By the same token the treatment of disease was heavily reliant on empiricism and magic. The early healers fulfilled a religious and spiritual role which modern doctors do not aspire to, and they did not have the armamentarium of tests and treatments which make the present day healer so relatively more effective.

This book attempts to chart the changes in attitudes to and patterns of diseases; in the knowledge and treatment of disease; in the training, status and lives of doctors and other health-care workers; in the home and hospital treatment offered; and in the organisation and administration of medical services; and it does so in the context of the County of Caithness, a unique and fascinating part of Scotland.

And so the story runs from the days of amulets – various objects worn about the person as charms against disease or evil – to the era of isotopes – forms of chemical element, some of which are radioactive and used in diagnosis and treatment in modern medicine.

Inevitably the account is patchy and incomplete. Evidence and records from the early days are scanty or non-existent. Even from modern times records which one would have expected to be available are disappointingly missing. Nevertheless the story shows, to a hopefully acceptable degree, the changes in medicine in Caithness and the dedication of generations of doctors who practised it.

D.H.A.B
Edinburgh, 1998

CHAPTER ONE

The Early Days

Medicine Before Records – The People

THAT PART OF THE BRITISH ISLES which is now Scotland first saw human settlement about 9,000 years ago. Those people occupied a land not long freed from the grip of ice but one which was rich in the essentials for their existence – food, water, fuel and materials for shelter and clothing.[1] They came, tentatively at first, as visitors probably from Ireland and then as settlers.[2] Many arrived from continental Europe by land over what is now the southern part of the North Sea, and others by boat to coastal sites.[3] They spread gradually northwards and lived by hunting, fishing and gathering, in rough temporary shelters.[4] This period, before 4000 BC and labelled Mesolithic by archaeologists, has left little trace in Caithness except a settlement at Keiss but as Wickham-Jones points out, sites in Caithness in particular may be difficult to find because of the build-up of peat over old land surfaces.[5]

In Europe, the spread of communities which had developed farming and animal husbandry – the Neolithic way of life – occurred between 5000 and 3000 BC with Caithness again participating a little later than other regions. This was the age of chambered tombs of which there are 67 in Caithness[6] probably dating to the 3rd millennium BC.[7] Later and with the advance of technology, the Bronze age dawned although in the earlier period flint implements were still being used. The important artefacts of this age are the standing stone settings of which there are numerous examples in Caithness.[8] About 1500 BC there is evidence of burials in cists and, from 1000 BC, of cremations. It is only in the late Bronze age, around 500 BC however that remains of settlements of any significance are to be found.

The brochs of which there are the remains of 110 in Caithness, are related to the Iron Age with its increasingly sophisticated stock-raising and agriculture. J.I. Bramman in *The Caithness Book* mentions the locally known 'wags' – stone-walled houses with attached chambers – as also belonging to the period.[9] By the 4th century AD the area had become under Pictish influence and several Pictish symbol stones are to be found in Caithness. The problem of Pictish and Celtic speaking peoples in Caithness is discussed by McCallum in a chapter of *The Caithness Book* emphasising how relatively little is known of these people in the county.[10]

Pre-history is defined as that part of the human story before writing. The Picts and Celts evolved an alphabet consisting of straight or diagonal strokes, producing scripts known as oghams, which were used for writing messages and letters, often on wooden staves, but also for inscriptions on shields and tombstones.[11] Two of the Caithness stones have inscriptions but they tell us nothing of the daily lives of these people and certainly nothing of their attitudes to disease. The Picts of course became Christianised. St Fergus may have been a Pict and he probably attended a council in Rome in 721 AD. By the following century, the Vikings had arrived in Caithness and there followed a more documented era.

Their Knowledge of Medicine

In the absence of documentation, knowledge of disease and injury and their treatment can only be gleaned from human remains (which are in effect skeletal) or from implements used in treatment. By inference primitive societies in the modern world may also give us clues as to our own practices in the past. Osteo-arthritis, a degenerative condition of joints, is common in skeletons of the Stone Age period. Evidence of bone tuberculosis is also seen and the effects of fractures and other bone injuries. J.D. Comrie has concluded that inhabitants of Scotland in the Bronze Age had the ability to treat fractures by splinting. Numerous prehistoric skulls show evidence of the operation of trephining.[12] This was often carried out with a flint scraper and involved piercing a hole through the skull, the healed edges of which testify to the not infrequent survival of the patient. Why was it done? It was employed in cases of fracture of the skull but also in all probability to 'cast out a demon', a situation where modern medicine might diagnose epilepsy, mental disease or cerebral tumour. Until quite recently primitive people in New Guinea and the South Pacific trephined for fractures and also to cure epilepsy and insanity. It has been suggested that those who survived the operation acquired magical powers and that when they died, bits of their skulls would act as charms or amulets against such disorders as epilepsy and mental illness.

Teeth as well as bones survive burial well and those from this period show much wearing, implying a coarse, gritty diet. Wear on teeth was liable to expose the dental pulp, with resultant infection and abscesses. Dental caries was rare.

It has to said that as far as Caithness itself is concerned there is limited evidence of disease from human remains found there. T.H. Huxley made no reference to bone disease in his study of remains from various sites in the county in Laing's *Prehistoric Remains of Caithness*[13] but Corcoran, commenting on the human skeletal remains found in chambered cairns at Loch Calder, in the 1960s mentions several diseases. Osteo-arthritis in these Neolithic people appears to have been usual in persons over thirty. There were three instances of osteomyelitis (an acute or chronic bacterial infection of bone) and one possible tuberculous infection of the vertebral column, the same person having suffered a prolapsed intervertebral disc. The actual cause of death in these individuals was not apparent although one appears to have died from having been shot in the back by an arrow![14]

More recently however, Dr Dorothy Lunt* has undertaken extensive and meticulous studies of dental material from sites in Caithness kept in museums and anatomy departments all over Scotland. Up to 1960 she was unable to find any skeletal material from the Neolithic period from the Bronze Age or Mediaeval period. One dentition was found from an Iron age long cist and 250 teeth from Viking sites (although identification as Viking is now considered doubtful in some cases). Her conclusion is that 'there is so little skeletal and dental material from archaeological periods in Caithness that it would not give any true picture of the state of dental health of these people.' An idea of what their dental health was likely to be can be inferred from the prevalence of dental caries in varies periods throughout Scotland (Table 1).

A qualification has to be made to the assertion that only bones and teeth survive long after burial. In Britain and other countries of northern Europe bodies buried in peat have been found in a remarkable state of preservation to the extent that confident statements about their state of health and nutrition in life and even the cause of death, can be made. Some bodies have been so preserved for 2,000 years, although in Scotland all have been post-mediaeval. In Caithness there are records

---

*Dr Lunt also records an interesting side-light on burials at Clow of Watten chapel. Some of these were head burials, the neck having been severed at or soon after death. She reminds us that the Celts had a cult of heads and hung up the heads of their enemies as trophies and that head burials are well known in Romano British and Anglo-Saxon England. But as the chapel at Clow can hardly be anything but mediaeval she admits, 'It's a mystery'.[15]

Table 1. Caries Prevalence, Permanent Teeth. Scottish Population Group.

	No. teeth present	No. teeth carious	% teeth carious
Neolithic	656	11	1.7
Bronze Age	1,306	23	1.8
Iron Age	538	22	4.1
Dark Age	2,203	78	3.5
Viking	307	9	2.9
Mediaeval*	23,560	1,473	6.3
16th–19th cent.	263	42	16.0

Figures supplied by Dr Lunt. *Updated 1993 by addition of Whithorn.

of two bodies being recovered from peat beds, but unfortunately, although the clothing was excellently preserved, only skeletons largely survived with some soft tissue remaining on the legs of one. The surprising difference between the excellent state of preservation of bodies in some areas, particularly Denmark, and the poor preservation in Scotland can presumably be related to different peat soil types.[16] The body found at Clayton Hill near Keiss was that of a young adult male who may have died of exposure and was buried on the spot and who, from his clothing appeared to have lived in the mid 17th century. At Quintfall Hill near Barrock the body was again that of an adult male whose skull showed the mark of a heavy blow and who may have been a murder victim. From coins found on him he also lived in the mid 17th century.[17]

Apart from the foregoing conditions and procedures which might generally be termed surgical, it can be assumed that treatment also comprised simple remedies and applications which had proved on an empirical basis to be of use and no doubt the use of plants, with an obvious effect on the body or mind. Mary Beith records that the shrivelled outer skins of a type of puffball mushroom have been found at Skara Brae, the 5,000-year-old Stone age village in Orkney.[18] This would point to the probability of the knowledge of herbal medicine. The inner flesh of the fungus may have been used to control bleeding from a wound and the spores to induce a degree of anaesthesia.

The Practitioners of Medicine

It has been claimed that medicine men or magicians were the oldest professionals in the evolution of society (despite similar claims from others!). They may have had a role similar to the 'witch doctor' of more recent times in some African societies, their activities being related to the current beliefs on the nature and causation of disease and to attitudes to death itself. It is likely that disease was regarded as the result of dire influence introduced by a god or by a living or dead human being, or the tampering with or appropriation of the person's 'soul'. The concept of supernatural causes of disease may well have resulted in some treatment methods akin to those employed by psychotherapists today. The supernatural probably involved the medicine man in priestly duties implying religious rites as part of his stock-in-trade.[19]

All of these activities probably involved the ingestion by the patient of animal or plant materials and the use of physical measures such as massage to induce evil spirits to leave the body as well as exorcism and incantation. The discovery of remedies including the swallowing of materials must have been a long, agonising process of trial and error but has been the basis of modern herbalism. Remedies were not always swallowed, however; some were worn or carried.

Charms, Amulets and Talismans

All of these were worn to ward off evil, diseases and witchcraft, the talisman being an object engraved with figures or characters which from Christian times could be a biblical text. The objects worn were of a varied and sometimes bizarre nature. A bezoar stone (a concretion found in the stomach or intestine of some animals) from a goat's intestine was regarded as a sure defence against poisoning.[20] Another amulet known as a 'snake-stone' or 'serpent-stone' may have been introduced to the early Pictish peoples by traders from the East.[21] These were coloured stones and pieces of glass, possibly obtained from an ancient burial site, although it is also suggested that some could be fossil ammonites. It is common knowledge that the 'charm' in relation to the prevention and treatment of disease persisted into historical and indeed, modern times. The raw potato, the hare's foot and the copper bangle are known to many people today.

Roman and Early Christian Influences

Caithness had no direct Roman contact. Tribes in the south of Scotland did, however, even if it was only on a basis of warfare and it is possible that medical and surgical practices may have percolated slowly northwards. Surgeons attached to Roman troops had an array of well fashioned instruments[22] and performed amputations, arrested bleeding with forceps and ligatures and sutured wounds. They also performed non-emergency surgery such as the repair of hernias and cataract operations. Roman practitioners were also knowledgeable in their use of medicaments, some of which are used in modern times. Such vegetable, mineral and animal substances as belladonna, liquorice, male-fern root, opium, alum, chalk, cantharides, egg white and fat, to mention only a few, were used. Comrie comments that the southern part of Scotland always practised more 'orthodox' medicine than elsewhere, perhaps because of the persistence of the Roman tradition.[23]

Christianised Picts and Scots probably preserved medical knowledge and tradition as well as religious. The influence of early saints was in part due to their powers of healing, which in turn may have been related to the supernatural or miraculous rather than their familiarity with herbals. The monastery on Iona founded by St Columba in the 6th century AD, included a simple wood and wattle 'hospitium' where visiting sick could be looked after and treated.[24] The early monasteries may have included a small physic garden. The old pagan amulets were also adopted by the early Christians and given a Christian significance, a practice extended to healing wells and springs.

These developments have their echoes in Caithness in Spittal in the parish of Halkirk, deriving its name from the Hospital of St Magnus, and also the bodies of water, such as the Loch of Hielan, the waters of which had a reputation of healing virtues.[25] But of these more will be said later.

In summary, our knowledge of the prevalent diseases, the practice of medicine and its practitioners is disappointingly meagre in prehistoric times. Archaeological evidence is scanty, particularly from Caithness, and we can do little but exercise our imaginations on tantalisingly little fact.

CHAPTER TWO

The Beginning of Records

The First Hospital

SPITAL (OR SPITTAL) is a not uncommon place name in Scotland and is an old form of hospital or hospice. According to J.B. Johnson in *Place Names of Scotland*, it was first recorded in 1160.[1] In Caithness the only place with this name is in the parish of Halkirk and derives from the hospital dedicated to St Magnus, whose chapel was close by. The first reference to this building is in a charter dated 1476.[2] In 1909 Donald Beaton wrote that the chapel 'lies about 100 yards north of Spital Mains farm and house' and that 'the eastern gable to it is still standing'.[3] About a century earlier a sketch plan of the chapel and what purports to be a sketch of the hospital were made by Lieutenant-General Hutton (Plates 1 & 2). Whether these relate to the same building is not clear but they were manifestly very simple structures. However, there is an earlier reference to a hospital in Caithness. In Caithness and Sutherland Records there is a petition on behalf of William of Forres, Dean of Caithness, to Pope Innocent VI at Avignon dated 11th February 1358 as follows:

> For confirmation of the collation by the ordinary to Wm.de Fores, advanced in canon law, of the deanery of Caithness, valued, on account of wars at no more than 15merks, notwithstanding he has a canonry and prebend of Brechin, the hospital of Caithness and a canonry of Moray with expectation of a prebend, from all of which he gets only 8 merks.

In his reply of confirmation the Pope refers to the hospital as 'a poor hospital in the diocese of Caithness'.[4]

Where this establishment was is conjecture. Miller in *The New Caithness Book* informs us that Margaret, the 'Maid of Norway' died in Orkney on her way to her kingdom and that messengers sent by Edward I to meet her spent the night of 3rd October 1290 at a 'hospital' before riding to Wick. He suggests that this was unlikely to have been at Spittal and indicates a possible religious foundation "along the east coast, possibly at Latheron'.[5]

Plate 1. Sketch of the hospital of St Magnus at Spital, drawn In 1815 (Reproduced by permission of the trustees of the National Library of Scotland).

Of course, care of the sick poor and giving shelter to travellers was regarded as a Christian duty from earliest times and the first hospitals were ecclesiastical foundations. Later, the control of larger hospitals passed to municipalities and by the 14th century many were lay institutions.[6] In Scotland, the 13th century was one of prosperity in the south and already the magnificent abbeys and monasteries of the Borders and Lothian were established and with them, their associated hospitia. In the north in the 13th century a priory had been established at Beauly and a Trinitarian order existed at Cromarty but religious orders failed to extend into Caithness to any important degree.[7] Nevertheless, some 'hospitals' existed as has been shown and were likely to have been influenced in their practices by their grander southern counterparts.

At the time of the Reformation monastic benevolence came to an end. In some instances the funds of the old hospitals were transferred to the kirk sessions of the parish churches on the understanding they would be used for similar purposes. Some disquiet was being expressed in 16th-century Scotland about hospital rents, as at a General Assembly in 1573, the Moderator 'inacted, that all Commissioners take a special notice how Hospital rents were used or abused'.[8] There seems to be no record of what happened in Caithness.

Monastic Medicine

The clergy of the day were those who chiefly cherished learning including a more rational study of medicine and they were instrumental

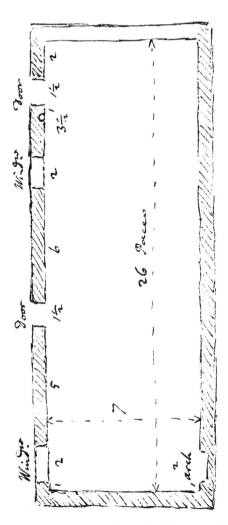

Plate 2. Plan of the chapel of the hospital of St Magnus at Spital, drawn in 1815 (Reproduced by permission of the trustees of the National Library of Scotland).

in disseminating knowledge through their manuscripts and libraries. A good example of a Scottish cleric who became well-known internationally as a physician was Michael Scot (circa 1175–1232). He was a translator of Aristotle, and was skilled in alchemy, astronomy and astrology, carrying on, in some ways, the association of physician and magician.[9] He would have used a variety of medicaments including aloes, balsam, amber, musk, pearl, gold and silver. One of the widely used prescriptions suggests an early form of anaesthesia:

> Take of opium, mandragora and henbane equal parts, pound and mix them
> with water. When you want to saw or cut a man, dip a rag in this and put it
> to his nostrils. He will soon sleep so deep that you may do what you wish[10]

One of the best known and best researched of Scottish mediaeval
hospitals is that at Soutra in the Lothians and much of the medicine
and surgery practised there would have been carried out elsewhere. The
reports on the researches undertaken remind us that the mediaeval
hospitals provided for the wayfarers and the sick, for the feeble and the
destitute, for the insane and for the leper.[11] They stress also the extent
of the practice of blood-letting – a practice which carried on well into
the 19th century – and that it was carried out for diagnostic and routine
or regulative reasons as well as therapeutic.[12]

It is possible however, that in Caithness, as in other places, the local
wealthy and powerful families derived most benefit from the few learned
physicians and that the commonality relied on a knowledge of folk
medicine, and 'skilly' people within their own community.

Special Hospitals

The Middle Ages saw some particularly virulent diseases of great social
and economic importance. They included bubonic plague (the Black
Death) and leprosy.

It was long accepted that leprosy was brought to Europe by returning
Crusaders but it is now entirely believable that it existed in late Roman
Britain.[13] It was well established by the 13th and 14th centuries and in
Britain it is estimated that there were then about 200 hospitals devoted
to the care of lepers. In Scotland there are records of leper hospitals at
Edinburgh, Glasgow, Stirling, Linlithgow, Kingcase in Ayrshire,
Aberdeen, Lerwick and Papastour in Shetland and elsewhere.[14] It is
hardly credible that Caithness escaped the scourge. There is no record
of separate establishments to cope with it in the county, but no doubt
the existing mediaeval hospitals provided some care as has been
suggested. In Scotland and Scandinavia the disease lingered much
longer than in more southern parts of Europe but only in Shetland is it
reasonably certain that leprosy in Scotland persisted into the 18th

---

*Richards puts forward the interesting idea that the Black Death may have
accelerated the decline of leprosy. He suggests this could have been brought
about by the plague killing lepers as immunologically deficient perhaps
(implying damage to the body's own defences against disease, a modern
example being AIDS), and also by reducing the total population.

century.[15] It is likely that the last native leper in Great Britain was John Berns from Shetland who was diagnosed in Edinburgh Royal Infirmary in 1798.[16]

Bubonic plague spread in great epidemic outbursts from its home in the Indian subcontinent. Most of Asia Minor, North Africa, the whole of Europe and some of the outlying islands such as the British Isles, Iceland and Greenland were involved between 1340 and 1352.[17] Thereafter, epidemics of varying degree of severity recurred up to the middle of the 17th century. Although Caithness was geographically isolated, the disease is readily carried by infected rats and their fleas, and seafaring therefore was also a danger in its transmission.

Scottish outbreaks were almost entirely the result of importation of the causative organism by sea from English and European ports, most often from the Baltic. The 14th and 15th centuries saw further outbursts in Scotland. In the 14th century there were epidemics in 1550 and 1564, and in relation to these Shrewsbury produces a map showing the places affected at these times; they are mostly in southern Scotland around the Firth of Forth and the most northerly place so indicated is Aberdeen.[18] Sometimes plague could be present in Scotland and not in England. For example the virulent wave of plague which followed harvest failure in some parts of the continent and Scotland in 1596 to 1598 did not reach England until 1603.[19] This illustrates another factor in the severity of the disease, namely the effect on a population either malnourished or frankly starving. In 1600 plague was active at Findhorn.

In attempts to prevent the spread of infection some Scottish towns had ordinances in place by the end of the 15th century, whereas the first English regulations came into being only in 1518.[20] Some of the regulations and the punishment for breaking them were draconian; for disobedience a woman could be branded on the cheek and banished, and a man might have his hand struck off and similarly banished.*[21]

Communities, in attempting to cope with plague epidemics, sometimes took possession of existing buildings to isolate the sick and sometimes built in haste, temporary and primitive structures. One can only guess that the latter was the practice in Caithness when plague struck as it was almost certain to have done at some time over the centuries when it occurred in these islands.

The Gaelic Influence

A glance at a map of the county, particularly with regard to place-names on the coast and in the eastern part leaves one in no doubt as to the importance of the Norse and Viking influences. By the same token, there is no doubt of the Gaelic influence in the west, not only by virtue of place-names, but of the persistence of the Gaelic language and culture up to recent times.

It would not be inappropriate therefore to suggest that medicine and medical practitioners in Caithness were in some way influenced by the Gaelic medical tradition embodied in the manuscripts, of which many are still held in the National Library of Scotland. Their content is however mainly of foreign origin, being translations from Latin and from the writings of the early Greek and Arabic physicians, or from texts emanating from the great mediaeval medical schools on the Continent.[22] The earliest date of these manuscripts is 1403.

These texts were used and owned in the main by two families of physicians who embodied a hereditary tradition extending over several centuries and who were attached to the great families of nobility in the north of Scotland. The family MacBheathadh had its name written in Latin as Betonus or Beaton, and in the modern form MacBeth. The other hereditary medical family was the McConachers. The influence and prestige of these families was great. In support of this, Mary Beith quotes John Bannerman who wrote:

> What can be demonstrated conclusively is that in every reign from that of Robert I to Charles I there were Beaton doctors, often more than one at any given time, on the payroll of the crown.[23]

The education of the Gaelic physicians was achieved not only by the study of the manuscripts, however; some also attended the great continental medical schools.[24]

The manuscripts give information on a wide range of medical topics. Some classify diseases elaborately and prescribe remedies for each, with advice about the weighing and measuring of drugs. Others deal specifically with leprosy, hydrophobia (rabies) and epilepsy, carbuncles and elephantiasis. Others advise on the management of wounds and the important art of blood-letting. More basic and general subjects such as anatomy and the questions of climate, diet and nursing and the examination of the urine are also dealt with.[25]

From all this, it is clear that these physicians were well informed and in touch with medical thought well beyond the bounds of the Highlands of Scotland.

General Picture

Life in mediaeval times in an isolated area such as Caithness must have been uncertain. It is undoubtedly difficult for us to imagine. The population, for one thing, was small, probably around 4,000 in the county in the 13th century and not infrequently disturbed by civil and religious strife. Infant mortality was high and life expectancy much less than now. Most people lived in miserable hovels and although they had at most times an adequate if monotonous (in our eyes) diet, they were subject to periodic scarcity of food or frank famine. But at certain times and in the uppermost stratum of society it is interesting to find that a contrary state of affairs existed. John Warrack, writing in 1920, just after World War I on domestic life in Scotland in the 15th and 16th centuries comments as follows:

> Such a picture as I have given of the life of the idle rich at the close of the 14th century – a picture which is borrowed in every detail from contemporary notes – must seem one of gross self indulgence. The eating and drinking appears indecent to those who have tightened their belts under the chastening compulsion of the Food Controller and indeed contemporary writers tell us that in these days surfeit killed more than sword and knife and the medical counsels of the time were largely directed against the perils of over-eating.[26]

Those few, of noble, powerful and wealthy families, were no doubt able to afford the advice of the learned ecclesiastics and physicians. The vast majority had to rely on folk medicine and the care of untrained men and women, recognised for their experience in various medical, surgical and obstetrical difficulties within their small communities. In the light of the state of knowledge of the recognised physicians, however, who is to say they did not fare almost as well?

CHAPTER THREE

The 17th Century: Some Health Hazards

LIFE FOR THE COMMON MAN and his family in Scotland from the Union of the Crowns in 1603 to the Union of Parliaments in 1707 remained frequently uncertain and at times difficult and dangerous. Civil and ecclesiastical strife was widespread and difficulties with communication and transport meant that crop failures, even local, frequently resulted in famine. Although Caithness was known as an important grain-producing area and exported meal, beef, pork and fish,[1] severe famines occurred in the county in 1634 and 1671. Of the former it is said that 'Multitudes died in the open fields' or drowned themselves in desperation.[2] Poverty, of course, continued to exercise a malign influence on health. The well-to-do and ruling classes were less affected by disease – better housing and nutrition being the main reasons – but this was often regarded (certainly by the ruling classes) as a divine dispensation! Of this age we have also to keep in mind that life expectation did not far exceed thirty years; that it was not necessary to record the internment of paupers or children and that infanticide and the concealment of illegitimate births were both common.[3]

The Diseases Prevalent

In addition to those mentioned in the last chapter these included 'fevers' (which may have been typhus fever or other infectious diseases), the flux (dysenteries), respiratory infections including the chin-cough or whooping-cough, smallpox, ague (probably malaria), tuberculosis (consumption and scrofula), and a host of other common disorders such as 'rheumatism', with which we would be familiar. It is said that the common ailments at this time in Caithness were the ague (which of course continued into the next century) and rheumatism.[4]

The Ague

Ague is a term of which there is now much misunderstanding. The word is derived from the French *aigu*, acute, from the Latin, *acutus*, sharp,

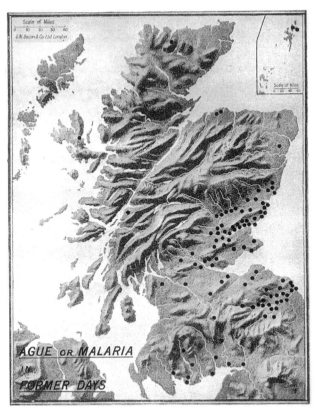

Plate 3. Distribution of malaria or ague in Scotland in the 18th century. Each 'dot' indicates a parish in which ague was reported. Note reports from Orkney and Shetland (From The Influence of Man on Animal Life in Scotland, *1920. J. Ritchie, Cambridge University Press).*

(plus *febris*): thus an acute (fever). The word was used by Chaucer and is an old term for malaria because it was an acute disease with fever.[5] Ague is recorded in Caithness; ague is accepted as an old term for malaria; therefore malaria probably occurred in Caithness – but this conclusion is quite unjustified. The conclusion, let it be said however, has support from what both historians and medical men have written. J.C. Smout emphasises the presence and prevalence of malaria in Scotland in the past[6] and Sir John Brotherstone wrote 'ague or malaria was one of the scourges of Scotland'.[7] Textbooks of medicine, in the early part of this century recorded 'ague' as a synonym for malaria[8] and maps were produced showing the distribution of ague in Scotland. The one reproduced here was compiled by James Ritchie from the comments of parish ministers in the *Statistical Account of Scotland.*[9] (Plate 3)

The present-day disease which we know as malaria occurs in tropical and sub-tropical areas of the world, and is known to be caused by one of four different species of a protozoan called *Plasmodium*. It is transmitted by the bite of anopheline mosquitoes. The life-cycle of the Plasmodium and the mosquito depend on a number of climatic and environmental factors chief of which are a minimum temperature, a preferred humidity and close proximity to marshes.[10] It is known that the minimum temperature allowing the development of the parasite *Plasmodium vivax* (the species which must have been responsible for any malaria occurring in Scotland) is 15°c and it takes sixteen days for the mosquito to become infective at 20°c. Preferred humidity is 60 per cent or more. In her study of historical outbreaks of malaria in Scotland, Kirsty Duncan used the mean monthly temperature record for Edinburgh (800–1900 AD) and concluded that outbreaks coincided with warm summers with high rainfall and that neither the average temperatures of the Mediaeval Warm Epoch (1150–1300 AD) nor those of the Little Ice Age (1550–1700 AD) appear to have limited the spread of malaria.

However, Edinburgh's summer temperatures do not correspond to Caithness's summer temperatures and, as Finlay points out in his study of ague in Scotland:

> The warm air of continental anti-cyclones penetrates to East Anglia and south-east England making the ambient temperatures there suitable for the development of indigenous malaria. A monthly mean temperature of 60°F, [15.5°c] for two consecutive months commonly occurs in England but never in Scotland.[11]

There is no doubt that true indigenous malaria occurred in the past in the marshy low-lying areas of south-east England and persisted into the 20th century. It is likely that malaria was indigenous in Scotland in the low-lying areas of central and south-east parts of the country. It is virtually certain that it did not occur in Caithness or in other parts of the far north.

Another factor in the discussion on whether ague or intermittent (that is, not continuous) fever was malaria, is the imprecision of diagnoses in those days. A number of acute illnesses are associated with sudden fevers (rises of temperature) with shivering and sweating. Influenzal-like illnesses may have accounted for some of the recorded cases of ague. Epidemic or louse-borne typhus fever, or louse-borne relapsing fever are alternative diagnoses. Q fever and brucellosis have also been postulated as possible causes.*[12] Certain it is that the use of the term 'ague' in regard to Caithness implies a heterogeneous group of acute fevers and no more than this.

As a footnote to the vexed question of malaria in Scotland it is interesting to note the comments of Revd Charles Rogers, writing as late as 1884, on life in the 16th and 17th centuries. He displays a remarkable degree of dogmatism and error. He writes:

> 'Dementia' is largely, though not exclusively the product of the marsh; when blood poisoned by malaria circulates in the brain, it initiates and corrupts its substance and texture. Insanity engendered, the victim transmits to his descendants a terrible inheritance. Passing one generation the malady may with renewed strength assert itself in the next. Marsh poison in madness taints for generations.[13]

Sibbens. 'A Terrible Disease'

Another disease which afflicted the people of Scotland in those times was one which receives scant attention in Comrie's *History of Scottish Medicine*, and no more than a passing reference in Hamilton's *The Healers*; yet is described as a 'terrible disease' in Pennant's *Tour in Scotland* and its appearance in any area 'struck terror into people's hearts.'[14] Sibbens (variously written 'sivvens' or 'civvans') derives from the Scots *siven*, the wild raspberry[15] (Gaelic: *suibhean* = raspberries) and is so-called from the raspberry-like spots appearing on the skin. In this it is similar to the present-day disease of the tropics – yaws (sometimes referred to as 'framboesia' from the French *frambois* = raspberry) and was also known as the Scottish yaws, probably because many Scottish seamen were acquainted with yaws in the West Indies and recognised the similar skin lesions.[16]

It is accepted that sibbens was caused by a type of bacterium known as a *Treponema*, similar to that causing syphilis, but that it was spread by non-venereal means. Spread was undoubtedly facilitated by poor living conditions – social, nutritional and hygienic – and it was found from the middle of the 17th century all over Scotland from Dumfries to the Shetlands. It is also accepted that it was introduced by Cromwellian troops occupying Scotland after the defeat of the Scots at Dunbar in 1650. Some writers have referred to it as 'Frambosia Cromwelliana' and

---

*Q fever can occur in cattle and sheep and be transmitted to humans by raw milk or inhaling contaminated dust; Brucellosis is usually spread to man by milk from infected cattle.

Table 2. Features of Sibbens, Yaws and Syphilis Compared.

Sibbens	Yaws	Syphilis
1. No primary lesion	Primary lesion	Primary lesion.
2. No buboes	No buboes	Buboes common
3. Affects children	Affects children	Affects adults
4. Throat lesions – appear early	Throat lesions – later	Throat lesions – late
5. Frambosian (raspberry) skin lesions	Frambosian (raspberry) skin lesions	Frambosian skin lesions rare
6. Contagious++	Mildly contagious	Mildly contagious
7. Smells++	No smell	No smell
8. Bones rarely affected and then nasal	Long bones commonly affected: nasal and palatal occasionally	Long bones; nasal and palatal only occasionally
9. One attack usual	One attack usual	Several attacks not unusual

'Cromwell's curse'. Fresh importations of the disease possibly occurred after the Union from garrisons of veterans from Marlborough's forces in Flanders. According to Morton there is no record of sibbens in England although yaws was recognised there.[17]

The first medical description of sibbens is credited to Dr Freer in 1767. The oral contact theory of spread is emphasised, particularly with regard to kissing, the sharing of eating and drinking utensils and, in the Cromwellian context, the habit of Cromwell's troops of sharing their tobacco pipes when fraternising with locals. Following infection, spread was encouraged by the conditions mentioned above; 'sibbens are the engendered product of rank uncleanliness, fed and fostered by unwholesome food and filth' (Hibbert).[18] Disease occurring around the mouth was particularly troublesome for infants and it is recorded that babies 'perished for hunger, not being able to suck or swallow'.[19] Reddish, spongy (raspberry-like) skin lesions developed on all parts of the body and frequently spread and ulcerated. Involvement of bones and buboes (swelling of lymphatic glands, especially in the groins) were not uncommon. The disease persisted, although with less frequency, into the 18th century, but the last recorded case occurred in Banff in 1851.[20] A summary of the features of sibbens and a comparison with yaws and syphilis is given in Table 2. This was compiled by Jonathan Hutchinson who was probably wrong in suggesting the absence of a primary lesion.[21] He was certainly wrong in his 'firm conviction that yaws was syphilis modified by race and climate'.[22]

With recognition of the extremely contagious nature of the disease, victims were often isolated in huts built in fields. Mercury, usually given by mouth as the sublimate, was seen as the treatment of choice, and as long as it was continued for two or three weeks, it appeared to be beneficial. Acceptance of the need for good nourishment and cleanliness also contributed to recovery, which cannot be said for the almost universal practice of purging and blood-letting. Contributors to the Statistical Accounts of Scotland have mentioned sibbens but none from the parishes of Caithness; and other sources are similarly uninformative. It is possible that sibbens, perhaps in an atypical form, could have been mistaken for other diseases, but it is stretching credulity too far to suggest that Caithness escaped the scourge, particularly as the county had a Cromwellian garrison of its own. In 1651 Cromwell's troops moved north into the northern counties of Scotland where they:

> planted a strong garrison in the Tower of Ackergill and parties of them would seem to have been distributed here and there over the county and to have remained in it for some time.

Calder further comments that:

> Cromwell's troops are represented in history as rigid sectarians of the most severe cast...but it would seem that such of them at least as came to John-o-Groats were not so very strict.[23]

This is further borne out by entries in the Parish Registers of Canisbay.[24] A daughter is 'begotten in fornication' to William Mendtheplay in 1653 and another to George Dreap in 1656. Canisbay Session Records, as transcribed by Morris Pottinger,[25] record the misbehaviour of Cromwell's soldiers, for example:

Thomas Carre – 'under cloathes with Kath Barnetsone'
Johne Gudelad – 'carnal with Effie Donaldson'
Capt. Wood – 'making plays, drink in Adam Seaton's'

The local population did not of course escape censure as evidenced by the following entries:

Isobel Ham – 'confessed fornication with ane Englishman'
Margaret Mowat – 'again scandalous with souldiers is ordained to be put in ye joggs'

These entries relate mainly to sexual misconduct and we know that sibbens was not a sexually transmitted disease. Nevertheless, it is clear evidence of enthusiastic fraternisation which with the poor hygiene and possible nutritional deficiencies of the time would have allowed the rapid dissemination of sibbens.

Another entry in the Canisbay Session Records records a complaint that Helen Ruge called Isobel Gills 'a scabbed lyper' (leper). It is unlikely that at this time – 1654 – she was a leper and more likely that it was used simply as a term of abuse. She could, of course, have had one of several skin diseases but could she have had sibbens?'

Scrofula

As has been noted, tuberculosis is an ancient disease, evidence of bone infection being found in prehistoric skeletal remains. Pulmonary tuberculosis (phthisis, or consumption) and scrofula (sometimes called struma and King's Evil) reached a peak in England in the late 18th century but it reached to more remote areas like the Highlands of Scotland, probably only in the recent past.[26] Scrofula – tuberculosis of skin and lymph glands, particularly of the neck, was known as the King's Evil,[27] as it was thought to be cured by the touch of the monarch – the 'Royal Touch'. Although Charles I in 1633 at Holyrood is said to have cured 100 persons of 'cruelles or king's eivill', it is unlikely that the people of Caithness could have availed themselves of this benefit.

The Providers of Medical Care

Some changes took place in the type of medical personnel in this century, but not dramatic ones, and they did so in the context of a country which was very poor. Thus, there were few opportunities for medical education, and travelling to obtain medical attention was restricted. In country districts medical practitioners were extremely sparse. So it was that the local clergymen or laird often professed and made available rudimentary medical knowledge which was frequently acquired during their college courses. The towns and large burghs were the preserves of the physician with a university education in one of the European medical schools, but they also were the haunts of the itinerant quacks. Some Scottish burghs at this time made part-time appointments of surgeons or surgeon-apothecaries to treat the poor; in Inverness a Dr Mackenzie was appointed as its first municipal doctor in 1680.[28]

Perhaps some explanation of the different titles for medical men and their function, training and status may be in order. For many centuries care of the sick was in the hands of monks, clerics and the hospitia. A Papal edict banning clerics from performing operations which implied contact with blood was the reason why they employed as deputies their barber colleagues who of course shaved but also practised blood-letting or phlebotomy. A Guild of Surgeons and Barbers was incorporated in Edinburgh in 1505. This separation of medicine and surgery resulted in the emergence of another specialty interested in the use of drugs (materia medica) – the apothecaries. In Scotland some surgeons combined these functions and became surgeon-apothecaries; others were barber-surgeons.

Surgeons and apothecaries were trained by apprenticeship lasting three to five years, and this was usually formalised by written agreement (often with numerous prohibitions against 'drunkenness, fornication and haunting of taverns.'!).[29] Their functions included the treatment of wounds and fractures, teeth extractions, amputations, blood-letting, but also skin diseases and embalming the dead. Some surgeons became skilled at couching for cataracts (displacing the opaque lens into the vitreous part of the eye), cutting for bladder stones (a common disease in those times) and the release of hernias. One of the benefactions of the elders of the Kirk to the poor of Wick about this time included 'three pounds' [presumably Scots] 'for ye payment of ye physician qt cutt a certain poor man in ye country, for ye gravel' [small bladder stones].[30] Those who aspired to become physicians eventually found the direct association of medicine with clerics inappropriate but continued to place emphasis on a broad academic education. W.S. Craig points out that an incidental result of this different approach to training was that 'socially the physician was recognised as a gentleman, the surgeon accepted as a handicraftsman'.[31]

The vast majority of the peasantry (and most Scotsmen at this time were peasants) would have depended, as previously, on folk medicine and its practitioners. These folk-healers, especially the old women in the community, ran the danger of the accusation of being witches, their persecution being a loathsome social disease of the time. However, T.C. Smout points out that some areas were always immune:

> Over the whole of the Hebrides and most of the mainland Highlands (except Perthshire) witchcraft trials were unheard of even in the worst years of the seventeenth century.[32]

This may have been due, in part, to a decision in the early part of the century that all charges be first reviewed in Edinburgh. Nevertheless, the last burning of a witch in Scotland took place in Dornoch in 1727.[33]

Although no unequivocal records exist it is most unlikely that physicians trained in the prestigious continental medical schools practised in Caithness in the 17th century. It is likely that the more prosperous landowners and merchants of the burghs had access to apothecaries and surgeon-apothecaries. The bulk of the population depended on self-help, folk-healing and perhaps the occasional chicanery of quacks and mountebanks.

CHAPTER FOUR

The 18th Century: Individuals Emerge

THE HISTORY OF any activity is made more interesting and satisfying if individual people associated with it can be identified and named. Only in this century are Caithnessians so revealed in the practice of medicine. Some were natives of the county serving their own community; others left to practise elsewhere; a few may have been strangers who came to work in Caithness.

The county they worked in was still remote, its degree of prosperity relative. A modern historian, A.J. Youngson, writing of Scotland after the '45 rising, mentions the export of corn and fish from Caithness to ports on the east coast as far as London, and that in its development it was, like much of Argyll and the lowland ports of Perthshire, 'always in advance of the rest of the Highlands'.[1] Contemporary observers describe conditions, particularly relating to the inhabitants, according to their own perspectives. In 1734 when the Revd Alexander Pope became minister of Reay, it was said that 'the parish was almost in a state of semi-barbarism, the natives in general being grossly ignorant, disorderly and intractable'.[2] When Robert Forbes, Bishop of Brechin, made his episcopal visitation to Caithness in 1762, he wrote:

> I had been advised to take a dyed loaf* or some good bread along with me when entering into Caithness being so poor and despicable a County that I could have no good thing to eat in it.[3]

Even more condemnatory are remarks contained in a manuscript in the British Museum, edited by Andrew Lang in 1898. The author is unknown but is possibly a Mr Bruce, a Government official employed in 1749 to survey the forfeited and other estates in the Highlands. He had pronounced anti-Stuart sentiments and clearly had no high regard for the people north of the Forth-Clyde valley. He wrote:

> In Caithness there are above 1500 men; but by reason of the prodigious slavery and poverty of the commons, more than half of them are but pitiful,

---

*or diet loaf – a kind of sponge cake.

half-starved creatures whom a stranger would hardly believe to be inhabitants of Great Britain. The gentry are strong and well-bodied men.[4]

Twenty years later, in 1769, Thomas Pennant made his famous journey through Scotland and wrote of the people of Caithness:

> The tender sex are the only animals of burden…The common people are kept in great servitude and most of their time is given to their lairds, an inevitable impediment to the prosperity of the county.[5]

Donaldson makes reference to a 'flood of intemperance' in the 18th century, and avers: 'Drinking, dancing and immorality were at this time the three chief recreations of the people.'[6] Aeneas Bayne, on the other hand, wrote, as regards the manners of the people in 1735, 'it is one of the best civilised shires in Scotland.'[7] As the century drew to its close, the *Statistical Account of Scotland* was published (1794).

The accounts of each county, written as they were, mostly by the parish ministers, show the contemporary scene in a less harsh light. The opinion from the parish of Thurso was that 'the people in general are remarkably sober, regular and attentive to business. Their only public amusement is dancing.'[8] The parish minister of Wick thought his parishioners were 'in general of the established church of Scotland, of good, moderate and peaceable disposition, not ignorant of the principles nor inattentive to the practice of religion.'[9]

Eighteenth-century Caithness Doctors

It is perhaps not surprising that the first medical men in the county who can be named are those mainly of prominent families who had access to education; the lowly apothecary and certainly the folk healer went unrecorded. These families were not numerous and showed features which tended to distinguish them from similar families elsewhere in Scotland. Donaldson in his introduction to *The Mey Letters* says:

> During the eighteenth century the peculiar character of the gentry of Caithness, who numbered about 70 families, was largely circumscribed by the conditions under which they lived. From a purely physical viewpoint they were more or less isolated from the rest of Scotland; for example, a journey to Edinburgh by road then required eight days, while politically speaking they were as we have already seen in the case of the Laird of Mey and as Andrew Lang puts it 'behind the North Wind of politics.' They had, moreover, no lot or part in the Celtic heritage of their Highland neighbours and it is probably on that account that their culture was Anglophile rather than purely Scottish.[10]

The sons of these families (if they did not inherit land and wealth) tended to make their careers in the Army (including the Indian Army and before that the forces of the East India Company), in the Navy, in Law as writers and advocates, as merchants (many abroad, particularly the West Indies) and in the Church. This was of course a pattern which extended into the 19th century and these men were among those who were instrumental in establishing and extending Great Britain and her Empire. Some, but not many, went into medicine, and some of their

Table 3. Doctors Known to be Born in Caithness
or Practising there in the 18th Century.

James Henderson*	Army surgeon. Died 1848
	Son of Benjamin Henderson, tacksman of Clyth
John Innes*	Surgeon in Edinburgh in 1638
	Son of James Innes of Thurster.
Dr MacKenzie**	Physician, Wick.
Alexander Murray*	Surgeon.
	Son of George Murray of Clairden and Castlehill
Arthur Sinclair (Dr).+	Died in service of East India Company
Arthur StClair*	Born 1736. Died 1818.
	Son of Wm. Sinclair, Merchant, Thurso.
Donald Sinclair*	MD Died 1873.
	Son of John Sinclair of Barrock
Jeffrey Sinclair*	Surgeon-General, Bombay Army.
	Son of Lt. Colonel Patrick Sinclair of Lybster.
William Sinclair*	Army surgeon. Died 1794 at San Domingo.
	Son of James Sinclair of Forss.
William Sinclair*	Physician in Thurso.
	Son of James Sinclair of Forss.
William Sinclair*	Of Freswick. Born 1748. Died 1838.
	Physician in Thurso. Son of immediate above.
William Sinclair Sutherland*	MD in Australia.
	Son of George Sinclair of Brabster.
John Williamson*+	Army surgeon.
	Son of Donald Williamson of Banniskirk
George Young++	Surgeon – apothecary in Thurso in the 1780s

* From Henderson's *Caithness Family History*
+ From the *Statistical Account of Scotland*, 1794
** From Pennant's *A Tour in Scotland*, 1769
++ From McKay of Bighouse Muniments

names appear in Henderson's *Notes on Caithness Family History*[11] and other sources. (Table 3) The earliest was in fact established in the *17*th century. John Innes, son of James Innes of Thursater, was known as a surgeon in Edinburgh in 1683 but he appears to have been one of those who spent their professional lives furth of their home county.* Of those who practised in Caithness, most is known of two Dr William Sinclairs, father and son. James Henderson perhaps belongs more properly to the nineteenth century and McKenzie and Williamson were much involved in the struggle to contain smallpox which will be discussed later. Nothing more is known of the others except Arthur St Clair.

Arthur St Clair, born in 1736, son of William Sinclair, merchant of Thurso, and a distant relative of Sir John Sinclair of Ulbster, had a particularly colourful life. He is said to have studied at the University of Edinburgh and then to have been indentured to the famous physician, Dr William Hunter, of London. But, as it was recounted that, 'he had inherited the martial temper of his race' and at the age of 23 he abandoned medicine for an ensign's commission in the Royal Regiment of Foot. He sailed with Admiral Boscowen's force to America in 1758 and carried the British colours on the Plains of Abraham. After the siege of Quebec he married a daughter of Bayard of Boston, and must have resigned his British Army commission, as he subsequently served in the army of the United States rising to the rank of Major-General. He fought in several battles of the American War of Independence and was at that time clearly regarded as a hero of the new American nation. Unfortunately an entry in the Encyclopaedia Britannica – 'St Clair's Defeat'[12] – records that in 1791 General Arthur St Clair was responsible for 'one of the worst defeats ever suffered by US forces in Indian warfare.' He was removed from command, and he and his family were reduced to poverty. He died in 1818 after a fall from a wagon.

Sir Stuart Thriepland. As one would expect from this epoch all the people involved in careers, including medicine, were men. The daughters of these families were expected to marry well and most of them did so. A few married doctors, one of whom was Dr (later Sir) Stuart

---

*Dr Matheus (Matthew) St Clair or Sinclair was even earlier, being born in 1654 and studying at Leiden in 1674. He was one of the original Fellows of the Royal College of Physicians of Edinburgh when it was formed in 1681 and became its President in 1698 and 1708. He was son of Sir John Sinclair of Herdmonston whose ancestor was William Sinclair, 1st Earl of Caithness. Matthew Sinclair had therefore but tenuous connections with Caithness.

Thriepland of Fingask. He was a remarkable man who was born in 1716 into a strongly Jacobite family. Taking the MD of the University of Edinburgh in 1742 and becoming a Fellow of the Royal College of Physicians of Edinburgh in 1744, he was appointed medical adviser to Prince Charles and was with him at the battle of Culloden and during the time the Young Pretender was a fugitive after the defeat. Thriepland managed to escape to France, at which time his father died and he succeeded to the baronetcy. In 1747, following an amnesty under the *Act of Indemnity*, he returned to a successful career as a physician in Edinburgh, being elected President of the Royal College of Physicians of Edinburgh in 1766 and regaining the forfeited estate of his father. He died in 1805 at the age of 89.[13]

He had the good sense to marry Caithness brides. His first, Janet, was the daughter of David Sinclair of Southdon, but after her death he married, in 1761, another Janet, daughter of Richard Murray of Pennyland. By the late 19th century properties were possessed by her grandson, Sir Patrick Murray Thriepland Budge of Fingask and Toftingall.[14]

In passing, it could be said that Caithness had less direct involvement in the 1745 rising than other parts of Scotland. Certainly, the medical men of Caithness had little part in it. A total of 64 doctors (including Thriepland) are mentioned in the list of persons concerned in the rebellion, mostly on the Jacobite side but a few with the Hanoverian forces.[15] None of these came from or practised in the county.

The Sinclairs of Freswick

The main reason why more is known of the two Doctors William Sinclair mentioned above is the existence of the Sinclair of Freswick Papers. These were part of the estate of Mrs Ferryman of London. They were offered in 1939 to Sir Archibald Sinclair, 1st Viscount Sinclair, who presented them to the Scottish Record Office where they remain. They are records of the Sinclair family of Freswick and Lochend and include many letters written to the doctors by their patients. In these pre-telephone days the patient could summon or communicate with his doctor only by letter or word-of-mouth, depending on his literacy.

William Sinclair senior, (?1711–?1776) was a son of John Sinclair of Forss, and was one of those Scots who received a medical education on the Continent, including the most prestigious medical school in Europe at the time – Leiden in Holland. Earlier in 1728 he had been apprenticed, for training in the practice of physic, to the Edinburgh surgeon and apothecary George Young, and during the three years of his apprenticeship he may also have studied at the medical faculty in Edinburgh. He returned to Thurso to practise there, leaving again in 1736 for Holland. In Leiden he attended lectures by the great Boerhaave and Albinus, but the following year he continued his studies at Paris. In 1738 he travelled to Rheims, where he took his MD, and thereafter returned to Caithness where he practised as a physician and apothecary.[16]

Sinclair's training in Leiden was not remarkable at that time. A total of 746 foreign students studied under Boerhaave from 1709 to 1738, most of whom had some education at a university in their country of origin beforehand. What was remarkable was the relatively large number of Scots (244) and the fact that both Scots and English preferred to use their pre-Union nationality title. (Table 4)

Table 4. Origin of English-speaking Leiden students 1709–1738 (From Hamilton, The Healers)

Angli	352
Scoti	244
Hiberni	122
Britanni	7
Colonials	15
'Foreigners'	4
Not stated	2
Total	746

William Sinclair (1748–1838) was possibly an MD of Aberdeen University, although no record exists, apart from his being an alumnus in arts 1764–68.[17] There is some indication of the form of his early training in a letter addressed to his father from Dr Livingston* of Aberdeen, dated 11 November 1765:

> Mr McLeod and I were of the opinion that it would be no loss to your son to come under the usual obligations of an Indenture. Most young men at his time of life should be under certain restrictions, which will not be

---

*Dr Thomas Livingston was physician at the infirmary on Woolmanhill which had been established in 1741. He was accoucheur to the Duchess of Gordon in 1768 and father of Dr William Livingston who founded the Aberdeen dispensary in 1787 and became Professor of Medicine in Marischal College in 1793.

rigorously observed upon my part...He has just begun to attend the Greek class in the College and should have liberty to attend the other classes during the course of his apprenticeship. Mr McLeod has become bound as his Cautioner...Young men in this place have daily opportunities of seeing variety of practice in our Infirmary of which I have had the entire direction for these fourteen years...Your son has already paid the Three Hundred Merks of apprenticeship fee for which this letter may serve as a sufficient voucher.[18]

There exists also a certificate (in Latin), signed by Professor James Robertson of the University of Edinburgh, that Wm. Sinclair, son of William Sinclair MD had studied such subjects as anatomy, surgery, theoretical medicine, botany, pharmacy and statistics between 1770 and 1775.[19] Sinclair acquired the estate by purchase in 1778, acquired Thura similarly in 1801, and as Laird of Freswick was 'believed to have a considerable sum of money in his repositories'.[20] The peculiarities of his character are recorded in some detail by the Revd Donald Sage who had personal recollections of him as a visitor to the manse at Bower.[21] He describes him as 'a most eccentric but highly ingenious man' who was known to the country people as the 'Black Doctor'* (because of the colour of his hair) and who was 'above the ordinary size, exceedingly handsome, with a fine open countenance'. He and a Mr Ross of Clyne had been fellow students at Aberdeen and were 'fellow combatants against the mob both at Aberdeen and Thurso'. He married late, firstly a Miss Calder of Lynegar and after her death, Miss Jean Sinclair of Barrock. Sage says that being long a bachelor and by his penurious habits he 'saved so much money as greatly to augment his already extensive property'. He goes on:

> At one time and in some of his numerous manors he used to be in bed for weeks and even months, sleeping away the most of his time and living on cold sowans, having no other attendant but an old woman as eccentric as himself and well known in the neighbourhood of Dunbeath as 'Black Nance'...At other times Freswick could travel all over the county on foot and quarter himself on every family whom he thought he could impose upon. With Smith of Bower and old John Cameron of Halkirk he lived at free quarters for many months.

Despite all this he was a popular and observant physician and the collection of letters written to him by his patients make fascinating commentary on social as well as medical attitudes of the time. The other

*By the same token his father was known as the 'Red Doctor'.

side of the correspondence is not available to us, which is a pity, but does not detract from the insight it gives us to his practice.

His workload is difficult to gauge. There is a note of 24 May 1780 that he saw 'Mrs Manson and called to see Mr Murray, Mr McKay, Barrock and Mr Gunn's wife'. On 22 September 1782 he saw 'Mrs Miller, Leith Bain, Mr Paterson, Jenny Miller, John Leith's daughter, E. Sutherland, A. McKay (almost well), M. Grant and Mrs C. McLean.'[22] Keeping in mind the distances he may have had to travel and the mode of travel, he must have had much busier days than these entries suggest and his popularity is suggested in a letter from Miss Katherine McKenzie of Glengolly who wrote in May 1782:

> Upon my word Mr Sinclair I have such a veneration for you that I neither can nor will think of leaving this place without your full approbation.[23]

There were no telephones to disturb the doctor's slumbers and communications must have been difficult at times but emergencies, of course, occurred, and there is no mistaking the urgency implied in the following; from Ben Henderson, 29 October 1784; '5 o'clock in the morning':

> Dear Sir,
>
> In the utmost impatience and anxiety I have been looking for you all day yesterday and surely thought you would be here last night. For God's sake hurry as Mrs Henderson is worse in every respect with the addition of a violent cough.[24]

The diseases he treated, as might be expected from the very general practice of the day, varied from the trivial to life-threatening by way of the embarrassing. James Bain writes from Wick about a sore throat and Mr Phin, minister in Wick, complains about an ear problem: 'I have been troubled for more than two years with a humour [sic] in my left ear…I am very much afraid it may prove hurtful to my hearing.' He goes on to describe discharge which is always more copious in the morning, 'and it has entirely relieved me from headaches.' Perhaps he had suffered an acute otitis media (ear infection) which had become chronic.[25]

James Geddes, writing from Mey in April 1790, voices his concerns about his wife:

> Sir, I would have done myself the pleasure of writing you four days after the medicine came to my wife but heard you was from home.
>
> She is done this day with the Syrup of poppies and I cannot see any alteration. Her breast is quite free of the black putrid flesh and has much

fallen down in the top and the edges of the orifice leaving spongy flesh without any feeling when washed which she does now only with warm water. It discharges a good deal of thin matter and is always unfixed and not nearer her armpit. Will the medicine sent be continued. I hope to hear from you and with great regards.

I am, Sir,

Your most Obt. Servant[26]

The poor woman probably had an advanced malign tumour of the breast. The Syrup of poppies, an opium preparation, would have been given on a purely palliative basis to relieve pain.

Janey Miller's health was a great worry to her father Alexander, who wrote from Staxigoe in 1769 that she had been ailing for about fifteen months. 'The cough troubles her much', he informed Dr Sinclair. 'She spits a great deal of thick matter and is much fallen off in flesh.'[27] We do not know her age, but it sounds as if she had advanced pulmonary tuberculosis, or possibly widespread bronchiectasis (dilation and infection of the bronchial tubes). A Miss McKenzie from Lilliebeg wrote in 1783: 'I am excessively distressed of late. The bone is come out but in all appearances theirs [sic] another coming.'[28] One can only speculate that she had a chronic osteomyelitis (infection of bone) with pieces of dead bone (a sequestrum) being extruded through the skin. From South Don, Robert Bain informs the doctor that his mother is getting worse and implores him to order something else; 'when she takes any meal she has no rest until it is all thrown up again' and she 'requires to keep a hot cloth to the place continually'.[29] Probably she had cancer of the stomach.

A letter that was clearly not easy for the writer to pen came from Lt. Wm. Gordon, Clerkhill, on 2 February 1783. He wrote:

I have lately returned from London…Mdm. Venus stung me with a most Poignant dart…To be plain, Doctor I have had a discharge these twenty days past…I trust in your well known abilities in the venereal as well as in all other cases. Please observe privacy as the people in this corner of the world would imagine that one of the Egyptian plagues was come amongst them.[30]

Despite the attempt at jocularity, the underlying anxiety and embarrassment are clear, and it is to be hoped the doctor's reputation was equal to the cure of an attack of gonorrhoea.

Some letters confirm the good progress made by the patient, but one of these is oddly annotated. Mr Grant wrote from Halkirk in 1817: 'Mrs

Grant is much better than when I wrote last. The cough is not so urgent.'
But written three times on the edges of the letter is the following:

May God } protect } me } frae } my friends

I'll } protect } myself } frae } my enemies.[31]

One letter, dated 23 June 1834 was from William Cormack of Reaster,
who was obviously not a patient but writing *about* a patient:

Sir,

By your order I have attended Brodie Nicolson and brought him twice to
the verge of fainting. The cupful of blood herewith sent will show the state
thereof. This is the eighteenth cupful – the nineteenth and twentieth are
not much better.

   The Blistering plaster wrought well but all means do not seem to abate
the rapid progress of putredo in the blood. I can proceed no further unless
in presence of a Doctor or surgeon. Pardon this freedom.

Sir,

Your Obt. Servt[32]

Cormack must have been a local bloodletter, and the relationship with
a qualified medical man is interesting. It was the practice to remove
about 100 millilitres of blood at a time, and after the twentieth cupful
the total blood loss must have been two litres. Little wonder the poor
patient was fainting! What was it being done for? 'Putredo in the blood'
is mentioned in the letter, and the diagnosis was probably what was then
known as putrid (or malignant or spotted) fever – the 'pestilential fever
of Europe',[33] most likely typhus or typhoid fever. The great William
Cullen had set out in his *Practice of Physic* of 1791[34] the symptoms in
fevers which denoted 'the putrescent state of the fluids' and which were
indications (among others) for bloodletting – indications which both
Cormack and Dr Sinclair were following. It was not until later in the
19th century that the dangerous effects of bloodletting were recognised,
but in some areas it persisted until surprisingly recent times.

Early Health Statistics

It is an illustration of advance in medical achievement that a disease
(smallpox) that was a scourge in the time of the Sinclairs is now
eradicated. *The Statistical Account of Scotland* gives us the first written
impression of health in the county, albeit a patchy and superficial one.
Of the ten parishes in Caithness only four are favoured by health

references by the authors. The people of Dunnet were said to be frequently exposed to cold, damp and excessive fatigue 'which brings on rheumatisms and coughs' made worse, their minister thought, by being 'ill accommodated in lodging'. Ministers seemed to vie with each other in putting their parishes in a good light from the health point of view.

'Not a more healthy county in Britain', wrote the incumbent of the parish of Halkirk. 'No disease that can be called peculiar to it. This county is the best nursery for the British army. Few districts where more good health is enjoyed than in Canisbay' claimed the minister of that parish. He went on to admit that colds, coughs and rheumatism were not infrequent, but that fevers 'prevail as little here, perhaps, as in any other corner of the world.' He mentions smallpox as being 'seldom mortal' and states that 'other diseases are extremely rare.' He ends his reassuring story with the sentence, 'Few parishes, therefore, give less trouble or emolument to physicians than Canisbay.'[35]

The reality was less rosy. The comments from the parish of Thurso were written by Sir John Sinclair himself, and he had the good sense to have observations on medical matters made by a medical man – Mr John Williamson, described as surgeon to the 2nd battalion, Rothesay and Caithness Fencibles – already mentioned. He writes: 'Fevers generally designated nervous and putrid are common', and he explained this by adding: 'From Wick along the eastern and northern coast to Dunnet farmers depend on sea-ware for manure…The putrefactive process is promoted, putrid effluvia being sent over a considerable extent.' He also noted that the flux (dysentery) was very common, but he reserves his longest and most sombre comment for smallpox – the worst of the 18th-century epidemics.

The Smallpox

Epidemics are frightening, but it is when a disease like smallpox smites an individual that the full horror is experienced by the patient and those about him. We need only look at another of the letters to Dr Sinclair to illustrate this. The letter was from Elizabeth Grant of Dunbeath in April 1821, but for some reason was signed by Chirston Grant. She wrote about her youngest son David who had suffered from smallpox for 22 days, during 18 of which he had been blind. She had been in touch with Dr Jolly (This was probably a Revd Dr Jolly who had some medical knowledge) who suggested she open his eyes; 'one of them opened of itself, the other I opened with my tongue.' She could see nothing in his eyes but a thick scum and 'he sees no light himself.' She concludes:

I beg Freswick will advise if there is any remedy and order the bearer to take with her any medical man you may prescribe for the purpose of executing it, and allow me to remain,

Very respectfully,
Your Obt. Servt.[36]

This desperate mother was coping with one of the severe complications of the disease. Pustules may form over the eye causing corneal scarring and blindness, or the entire eyeball may be involved, again with loss of sight. The boy, having been ill for three weeks, possibly survived, but almost certainly would have lost his sight. The measure she took – licking the child's pustule-covered eyes – seems to us repellent and highly dangerous. Presumably, if she came to no harm, she had immunity from inoculation or vaccination.*

Sinclair may have been regarded as an authority on smallpox. He produced, in 1824, notes which he entitled *Observations on the Natural Smallpox*, and which may have been intended for publication.[38] He compares and contrasts natural smallpox, inoculated smallpox and inoculated cowpox. (Plate 4).

Inoculation against smallpox – the practice of transferring a small sample of the purulent exudate from a smallpox victim to the person to be immunised – was introduced into England from the East in the 1720s and adopted in Scotland a few years later. Inoculation was beneficial but was not without its danger; a mortality rate of 1.3 per cent from the procedure itself was recorded in the 1760s.[39] Its practice in Caithness became well established, Pennant, writing of the county in 1769 records that 'Inoculation is much practised by an ingenious physician (Dr McKenzie of Wick)...but in all these places the small-pox is very fatal in the natural way.'[40] As mentioned above, Surgeon Williamson of Thurso made some detailed comment in the *Statistical Account*. He tells us that in December 1796 confluent smallpox became highly epidemic and fatal in the county and that in Thurso one in four of the inhabitants fell victim. He put forward a plan of general inoculation by collecting the inhabitants of a district together, which seemed to be successful in that over a nine-month period he inoculated 645 people. This was not without difficulty, however, as 'the peasantry held a religious prejudice against inoculation', an impediment that was countered by the clergy

---

*There is on record the case of a soldier who licked off the lymph with his tongue immediately after vaccination and developed severe smallpox from which he died.[37]

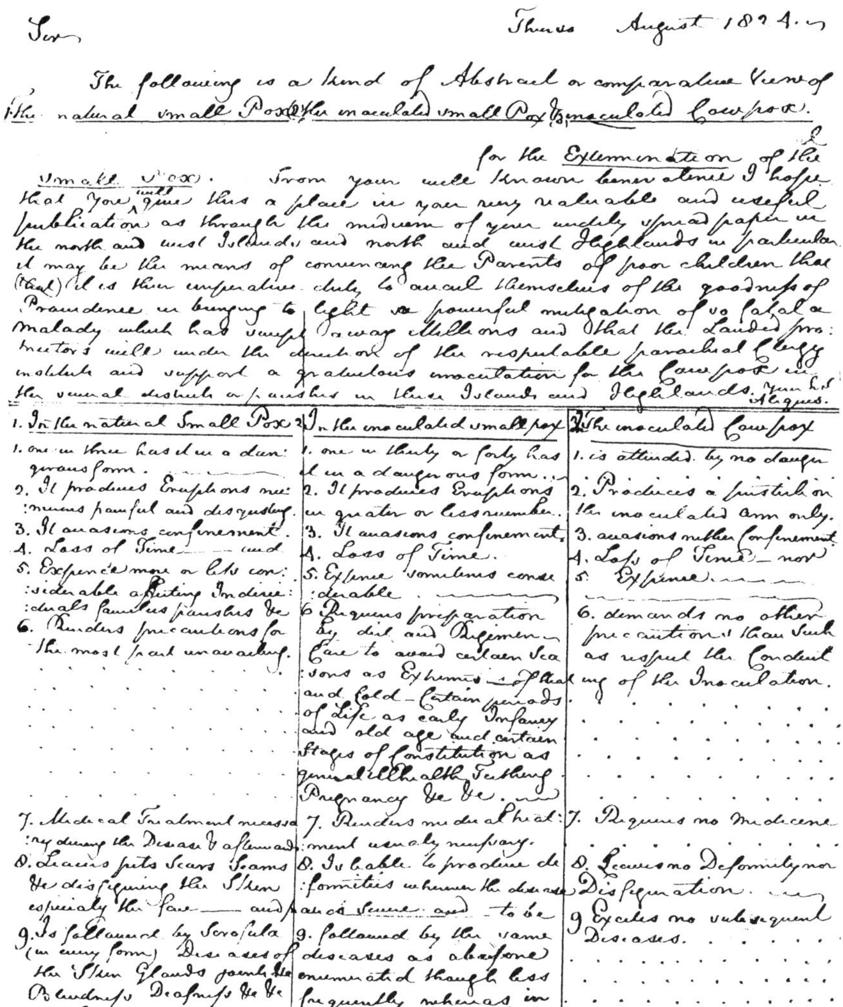
Sir Thurso August 1824.

The following is a kind of Abstract or comparative View of the natural small Pox the inoculated small Pox & inoculated Cowpox.

for the Extermination of the Small Pox. From your well known benevolence I hope that you will give this a place in your very valuable and useful publication as through the medium of your widely spread paper in the north and west Islands and north and west Highlands in particular it may be the means of convincing the Parents of poor children that (that) it is their imperative duty to avail themselves of the goodness of Providence in bringing to light so powerful mitigation of so fatal a malady which has swept away Millions and that the Landed proprietors will under the direction of the respectable parochial Clergy institute and support a gratuitous inoculation for the Cowpox in the several districts & parishes in these Islands and Highlands. Yours &c [illegible]

1. In the natural Small Pox	2. In the inoculated small pox	3. The inoculated Cowpox
1. one in three has it in a dangerous form.	1. one in thirty or forty has it in a dangerous form..	1. is attended by no danger
2. It produces Eruptions numerous painful and disgusting.	2. It produces Eruptions in greater or less number.	2. Produces a pustule on the inoculated arm only.
3. It ocasions confinement.	3. It ocasions confinement.	3. ocasions neither Confinement
4. Loss of Time — and	4. Loss of Time.	4. Loss of Time — nor
5. Expence more or less considerable affecting Individuals families parishes &c	5. Expence sometimes considerable	5. Expence.
6. Renders precautions for the most part unavailing.	6. Requires preparation by diet and Regimen — Care to avoid certain Seasons as Extremes of heat and Cold — Certain periods of Life as early Infancy and old age and certain stages of Constitution as general ill health Teething Pregnancy &c &c.	6. demands no other precautions than such as respect the Conducting of the Inoculation.
7. Medical Treatment necessary during the Disease & afterwards	7. Renders medical treatment usually necessary.	7. Requires no Medicine
8. Leaves pits Scars Seams &c disfiguring the Skin especially the face — and	8. Is liable to produce deformities whenever the disease proves severe and — to be	8. Leaves no Deformity nor Disfiguration.
9. Is followed by Scrofula (in every form) Diseases of the Skin Glands joints &c Blindness Deafness &c &c while	9. followed by the same diseases as abovementioned though less frequently whereas in	9. Excites no subsequent Diseases.

Plate 4. Notes by Dr William Sinclair. Sen., on Natural Smallpox, Inoculated Smallpox and Inoculated Cowpox (1824). *(Reproduced by permission of the Keeper of the Records of Scotland).*

who frequently inculcated in the public that 'it was a kind interposition of Providence to mitigate the ravages of a most fatal disease.'[41] The support of the Church was very important in this respect and included very practical aspects in that a plan was proposed that students of divinity at Edinburgh University should be instructed in the art of inoculation.[42]

Vaccination – the transfer of a living virus strain resembling cowpox virus to provoke active immunity against smallpox – was first introduced by Jenner in 1796, and in a few years came into general use in Scotland. This procedure was much safer and more effective and its universal application has helped to eradicate the disease from the world.

The Remedies Available

Medical men had few really effective drugs or therapeutic measures to combat the diseases they dealt with, but by the 18th century these medicaments were listed and standardised in pharmacopoeias. The one which would certainly have been used by the physicians in Caithness was the prestigious *Edinburgh Pharmacopoeia* produced by the Royal College of Physicians of Edinburgh.[43] The first edition of 1699 included some items which now can only be regarded as nauseating: *Album Graecum* was dog's dung and *Cranium hominis violenta morte extincta* was the skull of a murdered man – suitably powdered of course! It went through twelve editions up to 1864, acquiring an international reputation until the *British Pharmacopoeia* appeared. It listed the ingredients and preparation of Dr Sinclair's 'syrup of poppies'; *Syropus papaveris* (Syrup of poppyhead) – Poppy heads 1 pound, boiling water 15 pints and sugar 3 pounds. Its later editions discarded the disgusting.

We know that Dr William Sinclair, senior, brought supplies of drugs from suppliers in Edinburgh. In 1751 he bought £8 9s worth of medicines from James Scott, and in 1760 he bought 18s 11d worth of medicines and bottles from David Wilson & Co, The Dispensary at the Cross, Edinburgh. We also know, in one instance, how he attended and charged an injured patient:[44]

Mr Donald Douglas, Geise. To Wm. Sinclair, Surgeon.

29/1/1772	To dressing a laceration over your eye
	To dressing an artificial hare – lip with twisting suture & MrDent's approved bandage.
	To dressing finger much contused & lacerated.
	Cooling draft at bed-time.
30/1/1772	Visit. Replacing bandage.
31/1/1772	Phial. cooling julap
1/2/1772	Bleeding.
	Cooling julap
	Attendance till this date. £— 5s 7d

Self-help in medical matters was common, and books aimed at informing the laity on this were popular with those who were literate and sufficiently well-off. Probably the most popular and successful was *Domestic Medicine, or, the Family Physician* written by Dr William Buchan in the 1760s. In his introduction and writing of 'quacks, conjurers, charms and nostrums' he says"

> We make no doubt but the ladies, gentlemen and clergy who reside in the country will readily concur with us in endeavouring to root out such pernicious and destructive prejudices. Their example will have great weight with their dependants and inferiors.

His advice was commonsense and surprisingly in accord with modern thinking. Here he is, for example on the prevention of illness in children:

> Few things are more hurtful than sweetening their food.
> Children may be hurt by too little as well as too much food.
> Every mother ought to suckle her own child.[45]

There is little doubt that the lairds, gentry and clergy of Caithness would have acted in this manner to their 'dependants and inferiors'. An example of how a local family took responsibility for simple treatments comes from the McKay of Bighouse Muniments where, among many others, is recorded this remedy:

> A salve for any wound or burn.
> Take red wine   4 ounces
>   Oil   4 ounces
>   Finest sugar 1 ounce.
> Dissolve the sugar in the wine then put in the oil and boil the whole in a container until the wine is quite evaporated, that is the colour of it entirely gone.[46]

A Caithness laird who was known to take a genuine interest in the health and well-being of his tenants was Sir John Sinclair of Ulbster. Grant, in his biography said of him: 'To relieve physical pain was to him a labour of love', and told how his poorer tenants came down in carts to be rubbed for rheumatism by the Baronet's own hands.[47] In his later years he studied anatomy under Munro Tertius and the famous (or perhaps infamous) Dr Knox in Edinburgh, and chemistry under Professor Hope in the same city.

But as a reminder of how important a part was played in people's lives by magic and superstition one can read the Revd Mr Sutherland's account as quoted by Mary Beith of the 18th-century woman known as Fitheach, the 'witch' of Ballochly near Rangag in the parish of Latheron:

She lived in a turf hut close to the cemetery and no one knew where she came from, or even what her true name was. In this bothy she kept an assortment of strange objects so placed as to be in the full view of, and presumably impress with her powers, anyone that might happen to visit her. There were unusually shaped stones, rough clay urns, bladders full of ravens' feathers and cow's hair kept in a small case or straw basket.[48]

Finally, in the matter of domestic remedies, the place of whisky in Scottish and Caithness life cannot be ignored. Dr Williamson of Thurso summed up the perceived importance of the 'water of life' in the terse statement: 'Such internal phlogisties as pure whisky is generally adopted.' Perhaps, the common belief can be summed up in the old Highland saying, 'May the Lord preserve us from the disease whisky cannot cure'!

CHAPTER FIVE

The 19th Century: General Medical Services

IN THE MIDDLE OF THE 18TH CENTURY the population of Caithness was little over 22,000. By 1801 it was virtually the same, at 22,609, but by 1901 it had reached 33,870, with a peak of 41,111 in 1861.[1] The increases and fluctuations in population were related to the development of agriculture and fisheries and to the balance of immigration and emigration, birth rates and death rates. To cope with the overall increase in population there was an increase in medical personnel, although the details of this are not available before the 1850s. At the end of the 18th century statistical tables for Thurso recorded 'Physicians and surgeons – 3', the same entry commenting that they were all active young men and that they were 'the only medical persons in the county who have received a regular education.'[2] This suggests that the poor people still put great reliance on self-medication, folk-medicine and the local 'skilly ' person as well as on the benevolence of the lairds and clergy who professed some medical knowledge. In the last chapter passing reference was made to a 'Dr Jolly', a striking example of this type of public-spirited man. Thomas Jolly was minister of the parish of Dunnet until 1845 when he died at the age of 90, and Calder writes of him:

> There was no medical practitioner nearer than Wick or Thurso; and having a good deal of medical skill himself, he was for many years both the physician and the pastor of his people. He always kept a stock of medicines, which he gave gratuitously to the sick; and his manner of treating diseases was so successful, that individuals came to consult him from all parts of the country.[3]

He was alomost certainly the Dr Jolly consulted by Elizabeth Grant about her son David's smallpox. At Berriedale in 1837 the Revd Samuel Campbell had, as a student of divinity, attended some medical classes. He was known as a singularly unselfish man, dispensing 'advice, medicine and means freely amongst the poor of his charge.'[4] Much later, in Lybster, the Revd Henry McKay, minister of the Free Church congregation, also ministered to the health needs of the people, but he was in the unique position of also being medically qualified, and he eventually went off to do medical missionary work in South Africa.[5] The generally poor level of medical cover at this time, not only in Caithness, but in the whole of the Highlands and Islands, led to concern and the publication of an important report.

An Early Report on Medical Practice

One of those concerned was Dr Coldstream, a Fellow of the Royal College of Physicians of Edinburgh (RCPE) who brought to this institution's notice in 1850 a 'deficiency in the number of medical men in the Highlands and Northern Islands.' The College immediately appointed a committee to enquire and report, which it did efficiently and with care, publishing its findings in 1852.[6]

The committee obtained some information from the Board of Supervision for the Relief of the Poor which announced a grant of £10,000 from central government to the funds of parochial boards in Scotland for the remuneration of medical practitioners. The main source of information however, was a questionnaire sent to the minister of every parish concerned – a total of 170, of which 155 replied, and of these only 62 thought their area was adequately supplied with medical practitioners. Later, circulars were sent to 71 practitioners, mainly in those areas inadequately supplied, and 53 of them replied. From all this an important body of fact and opinion was derived. From the ministers came some surprisingly far-sighted and liberal-minded comment. They not only highlighted the dearth in many places of qualified doctors, but stressed the arduous nature of their work and their poor remuneration. The Revd Dr MacLeod of Morven, who happened to be moderator of the General Assembly of the Church of Scotland at that time, wrote:

> I know of no other class of men more inadequately remunerated than the medical practitioners of the Highlands or who obtain a livelihood at a greater sacrifice of time and labour. Some of them it is true, may have evinced a culpable degree of carelessness in advancing in a knowledge of their profession and this is not surprising under the many disadvantages of their position; but very generally they have been found to evince an untiring zeal and energy in prosecuting their professional duties under peculiar hardships and difficulties which disinterested humanity guided by sound and established principles, could alone animate and sustain.[*7]

*That these sentiments were widely shared may be supported by a remark of Sir Walter Scott: 'There is no creature in Scotland that works harder and is

This statement must also be a very early lay recognition of the importance of postgraduate education!

Many ministers confirmed that where doctors were thin on the ground they themselves gave advice and medicine and that some proprietors and factors did the same. In some remote districts the midwife was the only person to treat disease, and sometimes there was not even a midwife. The clergy, it must be said, advanced some intelligent and radical solutions; government should provide money to pay doctors in destitute districts; navy and army medical officers on half-pay should be placed in these areas; land should be provided on which suitable houses for doctors could be erected at public expense; small hospitals should be built in the more populous areas; a benevolent association be formed to supply medicines, to give some of the people themselves a complete medical education and to train nurses and midwives; medical assurance societies be formed in the poorer districts. Unhappily many of these enlightened ideas had to wait until the next century and the Highlands and Islands Medical Service, and ultimately the National Health Service.

The doctor's responses highlighted the difficulties they encountered. Almost all did their professional visiting on horseback; only 16 used wheeled transport and 17 had to use boats daily. Many complained of the inadequacy of remuneration; in some areas two-thirds of their patients paid nothing. Others complained of hard and dangerous journeys, of interference from unqualified practitioners and unjust treatment at the hands of parochial boards.

On the whole, Caithness had better services than parts of Sutherland, Ross and the Outer Isles. The picture in the county can be presented by the following résumé from the parishes which responded:

Bower. One medical officer – Alex. Robertson, surgeon, Whitegate. No deficiency. In difficult cases an MO comes from Wick or Thurso.

Canisbay. One MO. Eric Sinclair MD. Wick. The services of Dr Sinclair obtained by subscription. He attends at the manse one day a week.

Dunnet. No MO. Dr Mill and Dr Bruce attend from Thurso and Dr Robertson from Bower. The Revd Peter Jolly – son of Rev Thomas Jolly mentioned above – wrote, 'Several years ago my brother practised and resided in the parish but the emoluments proved trifling. The distance from aid causes problems. There are three midwives who bloodlet, not always judiciously.'

___

more poorly requited than the country doctor, unless perhaps it may be his horse!'

Halkirk. Drs. Mill and Bruce, Thurso. Replaced Dr Laing and Mr McLean who died three years ago of fever. A resident doctor would be of service; above all a properly qualified midwife.

Latheron. Three MOs. Mr John Bayne Lybster, Mr David McKay, Shantry and Mr Hugh Grant, Dunbeath. There is no deficiency.

Olrig. Drs. Mill, Bruce and Robertson. 'I have some simple medicines,' the minister wrote. There should be a druggist's shop in Castletown.

Bruar. Two MOs. from Wick, Dr Sinclair and Dr Smellie. There are complaints of inadequacy.

Watten. Nearest MO is in Wick. The minister wrote of the practitioner in Bower. 'It is doubtful whether he has a diploma!' There were few complaints of the want of medical aid but 'many of the exhorbitant charges of our medical men.'

Three doctors, Dr Eric Sinclair of Wick, and Drs Mill and Bruce of Thurso replied to the questionnaire. All mention the poor payment, but Dr Mill's reply, (reproduced in Plate 5) also mentions the difficulties caused by the poverty of many of the people.[8]

There is no doubt that this report brought to light the full picture of deficiencies of medical care in the Highlands. It brought forth many excellent suggestions and in its conclusion suggested that , 'The state of affairs is a reproach to the nation, in which all are implicated.' Like many reports, however, its immediate effects were limited, but it sowed seeds which germinated many years later into important and worthwhile changes.

Improvement in Medical Training and the Registration of Doctors

Before 1858, eight bodies in Scotland granted medical degrees or qualifications. They were the Universities of Edinburgh, Glasgow, St Andrews, Marischal and Kings Colleges, Aberdeen, the Royal Colleges of Physicians and Surgeons, Edinburgh and the Faculty of Physicians and Surgeons of Glasgow. The attainment of these qualifications required a period of study of usually three years and the passing of an examination.. But into the first part of the 19th century the degree of MD of Scottish universities, apart from Edinburgh, was not highly regarded, as examinations tended to be perfunctory or non-existent.[9] Moreover, it was only if he intended to practise in the Edinburgh or Glasgow areas that a medical man required a qualification; elsewhere he required none (although those wishing to be in good standing in the profession generally did acquire one) and he could obtain such medical knowledge as he had, by apprenticeship. This system had died out in

QUERIES.

1. How long have you practised in the locality you at present occupy? *For three years – and for twenty one years in this County 20 miles distant from this place.* –

2. What are the ordinary, and what the greatest distances which you have to travel in visiting patients? *My principale is within a circle of ten miles – but I have to travel upwards of 20 miles within the District under my charge and occasionally to go upwards of 30 miles in districts usually united in the charge of others.* –

3. What means of conveyance do you employ in going long journeys? *Always a Gig.* –

4. What is the state of the roads in your neighbourhood? *The roads are every where excellent in this County & a vehicle can be used except in very remote districts.* –

5. Is the position of medical men in general in your quarter improved, or otherwise, of late years?

From the social comforts of the people having generally improved within the last twenty years I consider the position of Medical Men to have been greatly ameliorated in this County. —

6. Supposing the people of the Highlands and Islands were generally able to pay for medical advice, according to rates usually observed in other parts of the kingdom, what extent of country in your locality would you regard as sufficient to occupy a single practitioner fully? *This being a thickly populated agricultural, mercantile, & fishing community – with the exception of the extreme South & western part – I am unable to say what extent of county in this locality would be sufficient to occupy a single practitioner.*

7. Mention, if you please, any special hardships incident to your situation, such as you think might be remedied by some general measure or enactment? *The only special hardship incident to my situation is the great distance I have to travel to the western, or Sutherland portion of the parish of Reay, where there is a large population distant from this side 17-20 & 25 miles & from a Medical practitioner on the west side of 23 miles & upwards – The Eastern or (Caithness) part of Reay is situated within a reasonable distance – of from 6 to 12 miles. – In my Capacity of parochial Surgeon I have occasionally to go 24 miles – but am very seldom asked by the other inhabitants to visit them – however urgent their state may be on account of their poverty – I consider a Medical practitioner in this destitute locality loudly called for – but no one could live here unless supplemented by a Salary – such as is One of the present excellent & munificent Duke of Sutherland in several of the other localities his Grace extensive possessions. I do not think there is any place in this County that would require to be remedied by any enactment. Thurso 28 Augt. 1851. James Mill Surgeon Sprit 1827.*

Plate 5. Reply by Dr James Mill to the Royal College of Physicians' of Edinburgh Questionnaire (1851) (Reproduced by permission of the Honorary Librarian of the Royal College of Physicians of Edinburgh).

the large towns by 1850, but in country areas persisted for some years longer.

It is not surprising therefore that much thought was given to improving this situation, and many years of discussion culminated in the Medical Act of 1858. This laid down very important regulations concerning the training and professional conduct of doctors, and established a medical register to which a doctor's name had to be added before he could practise medicine legally. In 1845 a medical directory had been published[10] which was a guide to the recognised medical profession and therefore a step towards the medical register. A Scottish edition was produced in 1852 and it is from this and subsequent yearly editions that we first get a clear picture of the doctors practising in Caithness. The directory gives the person's qualifications and sometimes a few details of his previous experience, but it should be remembered that inclusion was voluntary, and that doctors could decide what information was given. Moreover, the address stated was sometimes a home address, with the doctor working elsewhere. This was usual much later and when a doctor was newly qualified. It can be assumed that the doctors in the early directory worked from their place of residence.

Caithness Doctors: Mid-nineteenth Century[11]

The Directory of 1852 lists doctors by address and many we are acquainted with from the 1850 RCPE Report. There appear to have been ten doctors working in the county, most of them with licentiate diplomas from one of the Scottish Colleges.* Some had interesting backgrounds. (Table 5) Messrs Bayne, McKay and Grant, mentioned by the parish minister of Latheron, must have moved by this time or perhaps did not have formal qualifications. By 1862 the number had dropped to nine, and in another decade to eight, which is surprising, since the population peaked about this time. In 1882, nine doctors were listed, but by 1892, 14 were recorded. In the latter half of the century the majority of doctors had an Edinburgh qualification, with Aberdeen and Glasgow coming second and third in frequency. They were not lacking in academic achievement, two having graduated MB at Glasgow and Aberdeen with honours, several having been demonstrators in anatomy at medical schools, and one, J.R. McLintock, having been an assistant professor of Materia Medica at Aberdeen. One had a certificate in medical

---

*It is clear that the minister of Watten's suspicions about the practitioner in Bower were unfounded. Dr Robertson was an LRCS Edin.!

Table 5. Caithness Doctors of 1852

Bower	*A. Robertson*, LRCS Edin. 1848. MO Parochial Board, Bower
Pultney	*C.J. Madden*, LRCS Ireland 1829, formerly Lecturer in Physiology, Anatomy and Surgical Anatomy. Dublin School of Medicine.
Thurso	*Wm. Bruce*, MD Aber. 1845. LRCS Edin. 1845. *Hugh Grant*, LRCS Edin. 1850. *J. Mill*, LRCS Edin. 1827. *D.S. Smith*, LRCS Edin. 1850.
Wick	*C.H. Graham*, LFP&S. Glasg. 1852. *E.S. Sinclair*, LFP&S 1820. Surgeon Parochial Board and Goal, Wick and Parochial Board, John o' Groats; formerly Surgeon RN. Member Geology Society of Orkney. *W. Smellie*, MD, LRCS Edin. 1842, formerly MO Hudson Bay Co. Settlement at York Factory 1845–49. Several contributions to medical journals.
Dunbeath	*G. Burn*, MD Edin, 1850. Parochial Board, Latheron.

psychology, and John Alexander was a certificated factory surgeon. In the 1870s in particular, working as ships' surgeons seemed popular, at least four having done so, and others had worked for enterprises such as mining companies in countries ranging from Newfoundland to Africa and Bengal. One had worked in the British Hospital in Paris before settling in Caithness, and others were involved with the Rifle Volunteers. All this was a reflection of the activities of the mid and late Victorian era and Britain's expanding interests overseas.

Many men and some women, either born in Caithness or of Caithness extraction are recorded by Mowat[12] as being notables and many of these are doctors who were active mainly in the 19th century. He records others in his *Bibliography of Caithness* and they are all listed in alphabetical order and with his comments in Appendix 1. More is known about the particular contributions to medicine or to life in Caithness made by some of these than by others. A brief account of some of these contributions follows.

John Alexander. The important work of Dr Alexander and his brother in general practice, but more particularly in public health, will be discussed later.

David Anderson-Berry. His father was minister of the Reformed Presbyterian Church, Wick, from 1856–73. He shared the religious enthusiams of his parent; among his publications was one entitled *The Seven Sayings of Christ on the Cross*.[13]

George Banks. He was a son of James Banks, shoemaker of Thurso. He studied medicine at Edinburgh, qualifying LRCSE in 1858 and LRCPE in 1860 and became an assistant to Dr Eric Sinclair. Later he opened a dispensary at Canisbay, an event which was celebrated, rather eccentrically, by a hare hunt in which the Earl of Caithness took part. This episode became known nationally being recorded in a contemporary issue of *Punch*. Banks was involved in the typhus fever outbreaks of the 1860s; and also in the 'Highlanders' riots' in Wick, when he attended many of the injured. As to his recreations, he was a keen golfer and curler. He died in 1921 at the age of 86.[14]

James Grant. He was a keen naturalist and wrote the section on the Orkney mosses in *Flora Orcadenses* 1914.[15]

Alexander Gunn. Mowat describes him as an eminent Edinburgh doctor who worked with Lord Lister but his professional association with Lister and his research is difficult to establish. The only Alexander Gunn in the *Medical Register* and *Medical Directory* of 1913, qualified LRCP&S in 1877 and MD, St Andrews in 1886. He is recorded as medical officer to the Amalgamated Society of Engineers, medical referee to Liverpool Victoria Insurance Society and formerly senior apothecary at the Royal Infirmary of Edinburgh. Logan Turner, in his *History of the Royal Infirmary*, mentions only one Alexander Gunn, who was a dispenser from 1870–77. Lister arrived to work as a house surgeon in Edinburgh in 1853, and did not really start his researches into inflammation and antiseptics until after he went to Glasgow in 1860. He returned to Edinburgh in 1869 and finally returned to London in 1877.[16] It is possible that Gunn was involved in a non-medical capacity, perhaps in preparing antiseptic solutions, but did he make an impression on Lister and was he persuaded to study medicine at a relatively late age by him? The Gunn referred to in *Some Caithness Notables* would appear to be the Gunn mentioned by Logan Turner as a Royal Infirmary dispenser, and the Gunn recorded in the Roll of Licentiates of the Royal College of Physicians of Edinburgh dated 3 November 1877 and 'born Lybster, Caithness'.

Robert Marcus Gunn. An obituary in the Lancet tells us that he was born at Rattar and went to St Andrews University at the age of fourteen. He transferred to Edinburgh University and graduated MA in 1871 and MBCM in 1873, having been taught by the renowned surgeons Syme and Lister, and the ophthalmologist Argyll-Robertson. Study at Moorfields Eye Hospital, London and in Vienna followed, and his interest in comparative anatomy of the eye prompted a visit to Australia to study the eyes of marsupials. He also examined material from the HMS *Challenger* expedition. Several important publications stemmed from these studies. He became a Fellow of the Royal College of Surgeons of England in 1882, and from then until his death was a nationally and internationally known figure in ophthalmology, being an authority on the use of the ophthalmoscope. Ultimately he was senior surgeon to Moorfields Hospital and ophthalmic surgeon to the National Hospital, Queens Square, London.[17]

James Henderson of Clyth. At the turn of the 18th century he was tacksman or tennant at Clyth. It was said of him that he 'cured hundreds of the living and thousands of the dead' – a reference of course to his entreprenurial activities as a fish curer as well as his medical practice. R.I. Mowat records that 'he had a dubious reputation of having been a vivisectionist. Under the south wall of the farmhouse there is a low dungeon-like cellar, and it was there that he was believed to have carried out his gruesome experiments. Beneath the house locals believed there was a cave leading to the sea in which the doctor deposed of his [bodies].'[18] Obviously local contemporary imaginations were vigorously exercised!

William Henderson. Henderson was one of the first to use the microscope in the study of pathological anatomy, and he is also credited with being one of the first to distinguish between typhus and relapsing fevers. In 1845 he created a furore in Edinburgh by publishing *An Enquiry into the Homeopathic Practice of Medicine*. He was forced to resign his appointment at the Infirmary, and his erstwhile colleagues, Professors Syme and Simpson, attempted to have him removed from the Chair of Pathology.[19] Perhaps he was sustained by Christian belief; one of his other publications was *A Dictionary and Concordance of Names and Persons and Places in the Old and New Testaments*. The fourth son of Sherrif Henderson of Thurso, his election to the Chair of Pathology reached the letters column of local newspapers, where it was pointed out that he was not the popular candidate, but that, being 'a comparatively young man and without influence owes his elevation to superior talents and qualifications alone'![20] (Plate 6).

Eric Sutherland Sinclair. We encountered Dr Sinclair of Wick in the RCPE 1852 Report and the 1852 *Medical Directory,* but he must have first practised in Wick in 1830 as the *John O'Groat Journal* of March

Plate 6. Dr William Henderson (Reproduced by permission of the Honorary Librarian of the Royal College of Physicians of Edinburgh).

1850 records a testimonial to him for his 20 years' work in the community. In the same journal of 1838 there is an acount of a forged certificate 'by an infamous gang' purporting to come from Eric Sinclair, surgeon, used by a woman to get relief from destitution![21]

Calder mentions that his natural history collection was in 'a very fine museum which will repay a visit' in the doctor's residence 'Montpelier House' in the suburbs of the town.[22] In the *New Statistical Account of Scotland* of 1845 he supplied a report on the ornithology of Caithness and of Wick in particular. An anonymous writer in 1931 remembered the doctor's elegant carriage. 'The coachman and footman both in tall hats with a cockade and feather ornament in the side were conspicuous figures on the high box seats. The doctor always wore full dress with a large display of white shirt front richly draped with flowing frills'.[23] The Earl of Caithness, Earl James, was a great friend of the doctor and he was apparently allowed on occasions to visit with him if it was an old person or a family known to him [but only where no risk of infection might be feared]. The same writer tells of a lad in the

Plate 7. Dr Eric Sinclair (From 'Times Gone Bye', North of Scotland Newspapers plc).

Gills district who suffered a bad compound fracture of his arm. The youth was strapped to a table, the fracture reduced, the limb saturated with disinfectants then splinted and tightly bandaged with no more than a glass of brandy for anaesthesia. He recovered well. The doctor was so popular in his young days that 'fully a score of young "Erics" were named after him in the town.' A photograph of him taken in his later years shows him in all his Victorian splendour and assurance. (Plate 7).

John Frances Sutherland His publications included *Hospitals, their History and Constitution* and *Mania of Intoxication*.

Peter Cormack Sutherland. A native of Caithness, he graduated MD at Aberdeen and became an LRCS Edinburgh in 1847 and later a Fellow of the Royal Geological Society. He emigrated to Natal in 1853 but before that had been to Canada, travelled up West African rivers on a guano ship, served as ship's doctor on a whaler in the

Davis Straits and was in the Admiralty party in search of Sir John Franklin's lost Arctic expedition. During the remainder of his life in South Africa, it appears that he did not actively practise medicine but was appointed Government Geologist and Surveyor General of Natal. When he died in 1900 he was described as 'one of Natal's most honoured colonists'. His publications included *Search for Sir John Franklin, 1858* and *Journal of a Voyage to Baffin Bay, 1850–51*.[24]

Dr James Mill., a native of Fife was one of those who responded to the 1850 RCPE questionnaire. He qualified LRCS Edinburgh in 1827 and served his community until 1873. His son, Hugh Robert Mill, DSc, LLD, FRSE, became a well-known geographer and was author of *Seige of the South Pole*, 1905, and an introduction to Shackleton's book *In the Heart of the Antarctic*.

Despite Mowat's diligence in recording prominent Caithnessians including doctors he clearly was guilty of some omissions (as all authors may be). One omission relates to a medical family which probably produced the first woman medical graduate who was a native Caithnessian.[25]

John George Sinclair Coghill was born in Thurso in 1834 and lived a remarkably varied and colourful life. His father, a military man, had served with a Highland regiment in Spain; his brother, J.D.M. Coghill, became a doctor, as did his daughter Agnes. Sinclair Coghill was educated at the Royal High School Edinburgh and studied medicine at Edinburgh University. While he was still a student the war with Russia broke out. and young Coghill joined the Royal Navy and served as a Surgeon's Assistant with the Baltic Fleet until the end of the Crimean War. He so distinguished himself as an undergraduate that he became, on graduating MD (with Honours) in 1857, private assistant to the Professor of Midwifery, Sir James Y. Simpson, but instead of pursuing an academic career, as clearly would have been possible, his adventurous spirit took him abroad. He was appointed in 1861 Principal Medical Officer of Shanghai and consulting physician to the General Hospital there. While in the Far East he was one of the first Europeans to travel in Japan. The strain of dealing with a cholera epidemic in which his eldest son died was a factor in inducing his return to Edinburgh in 1869. He resumed his association with Simpson, taking over his lectures during his last illness and was an unsuccessful candidate for the Chair of

Plate 8. Dr John George Sinclair Coghill (Reproduced by courtesy of Mr R.F. Coghill).

Midwifery after his death. By this time Coghill had become a Fellow of the Royal College of Physicians of Edinburgh. He lectured on pathology in the Extramural Medical School and then in 1875 moved to the Isle of Wight for health reasons becoming physician to the Royal National Hospital for Consumption at Ventnor where he spent the remainder of his professional life. By the time of his death in 1899 he had made many contributions to the study of tuberculosis as well as showing a lively interest in antiquities being elected an FRSA of Scotland. His picture (Plate 8) shows a man of assurance and authority.

James Davidson Mackay Coghill, brother of Sinclair, qualified as a LRCP in 1860 and MD Aberdeen in 1867. His share of the adventurous life included appointment as surgeon to the 2nd Royal Lanark Militia and medical officer to the Imperial Chinese Maritime Custom at Hankow. Later he was colonial surgeon to the Sraits Settlements and Medical Inspector of Coffee Districts in Ceylon. He died in Shrewsbury in 1907.

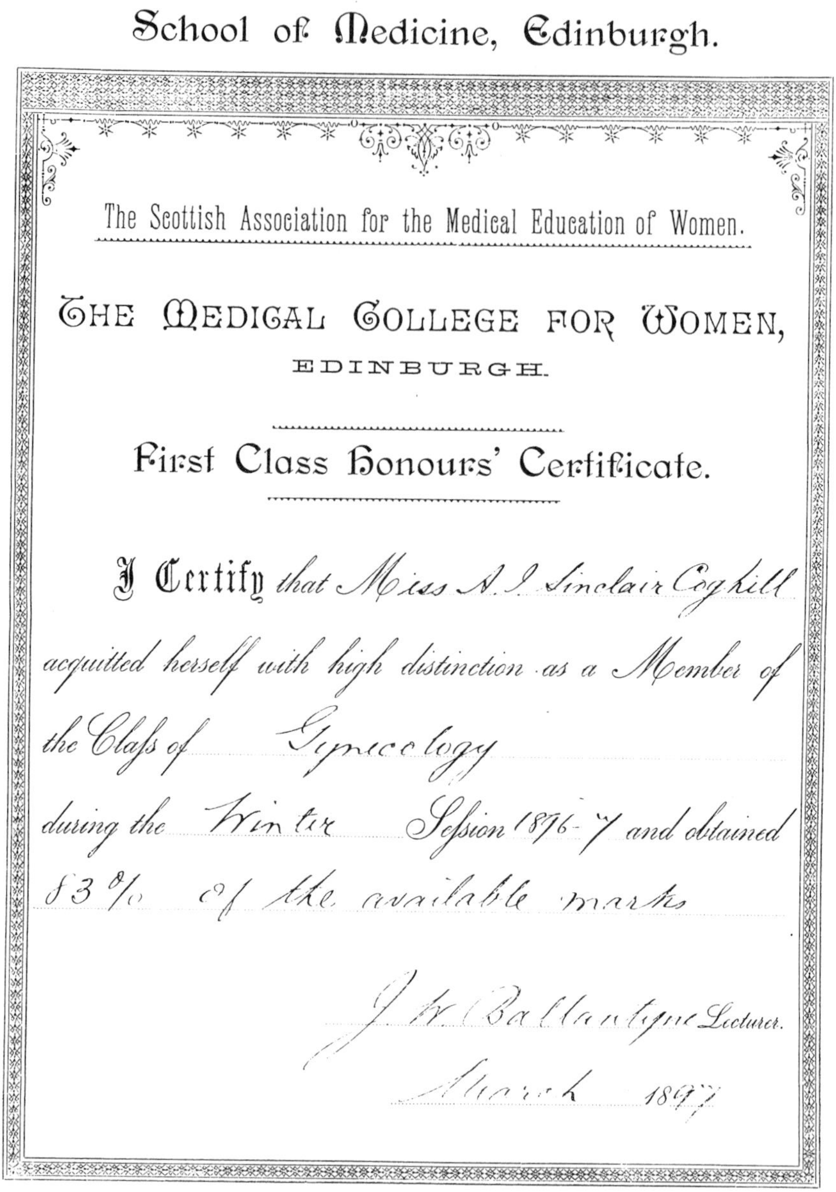

School of Medicine, Edinburgh.

The Scottish Association for the Medical Education of Women.

THE MEDICAL COLLEGE FOR WOMEN, EDINBURGH.

First Class Honours' Certificate.

I Certify that Miss A. I. Sinclair Coghill acquitted herself with high distinction as a Member of the Class of Gynaecology during the Winter Session 1896–7 and obtained 83% of the available marks

J. W. Ballantyne Lecturer.

March 1897

Plate 9. Honours' Certificate awarded to Dr Agnes Irene Sinclair Coghill by the Medical College for Women, Edinburgh, 1896–97 (Reproduced by Courtesy of Mr R.F. Coghill).

Plate 10. Dr Agnes Irene Sinclair Coghill (Reproduced by courtesy of Mr R.F. Coghill).

Agnes Irene Sinclair Coghill, was born in Thurso in 1872 and studied medicine at the Medical College for Women, Edinburgh, which had been established in 1889. This was in many ways a rival to the Edinburgh School of Medicine for Women which had been started by the renowned Dr Sophia Jex-Blake only three years previously. Agnes graduated MBCM in 1897 and was therefore an early woman graduate in medicine from Edinburgh. There is no record of a Caithness woman qualifying before this. She obviously did well as her Honours Certificate in Gyneacology shows (Plate 9). She married a distant relative, Percy Coghill, but it is ironic and sad that she died in child-birth at the age of thirty-two. Her graduation photograph (Plate 10) shows a young woman of formidable intelligence who in all probability was very determined and diligent – qualities which the woman medical graduate of these days had to have.

As has been noted elsewhere the doctor with formal training is generally well recorded whereas there is much less known about the humbler apothecary. An exception to this is George Nicol an old apothecary and druggist of Pultney. He was a good example of the 19th century 'lad o' pairts' who was sent to Edinburgh but managed to complete only one session in Arts and two at the Royal College of Surgeons. It was said that the study was 'too much for his fragile frame' and he returned to Wick to be employed by a Dr Stewart in his drug shop in Bank Row. Nicol later opened his own shop in Argyll Square which became a meeting place for the medical students on holiday in the town. He was well regarded by the Hebridean fishermen in particular for his treatment of whitlows (infection of the nail-bed or pulp of the finger) or 'day nettle' as it was known. He also dispensed many of the mixtures used in the cholera epidemics.[26]

A well-known Thurso druggist and chemist was William Bremner. In the 1870s he occupied the premises which later became the popular antiques shop 'The Ship's Wheel'. At one time he was chief magistrate of Thurso and is described as 'always dressed in a frock-coat and an air of melancholy'. He also extracted teeth, often in public, on the pavement in front of the shop. Two assistants held the patient firmly in a chair and Bremner hauled out the offending molar which he then displayed to the admiring spectators.[27]

Societies and their Role in Health Care

Reference has already been made to the difficulties of the poorest in communities in obtaining medical care. The 1850 RCPE report comments that doctors charged exorbitantly, but on the other side of the coin views were expressed – not wholly by the doctors themselves – that income from medical practice in remote areas was quite inadequate.

One way of combatting these difficulties was the establishment of Dispensaries. These were established towards the end of the eighteenth century and the beginning of the nineteenth century mainly in the cities and urban areas and were charitable institutions staffed by local doctors who gave free advice and medicines to the poor. Patients were seen mostly at Dispensary premises not in their own homes and sometimes there was limited provision for in-patient care. There is no record of such facilities ever existing in Caithness. Another way of tackling the problem, however, was the establishing of benevolent societies whereby the poor contributed very small amounts on a regular basis to a fund which paid for the attendance of a doctor. There is a record of a Friendly Society existing in the parish of Watten in 1819.[28] Its function was to aid members when sick and also widows but it is not clear whether it covered medical care or simply provided financial support. In any case the minister thought its 'advantages not very obvious'. In 1836 a Destitute Sick Society existed in Wick, receiving donations from 'proprietors and county gentlemen.' Its aims were presumably the same as the Watten Society.[29] By the end of the century however, Canisbay, for example, had a Medical Association. Its members were all house-holders and members of family over eighteen years of age living at home. The half-yearly subscription (which in the 1890s was four shillings) covered doctors visits and one shilling went towards the up-keep of the doctor's house provided by the people of the parish. The Parish Council contributed £98 per annum for the medical attention of those on Poor Law relief. Medicines were paid for separately, a quart bottle costing two shillings and sixpence. This association continued up to the time of the National Health Service.[30] Similar associations and societies existed elsewhere in the county. The society which was extended to Halkirk village in 1890 had been initiated some years earlier by the Spittal quarries.

There were other societies however, which had a bearing on how well or poorly patients were treated medically although not concerned with providing money to pay the doctor or support the sick financially. These were the professional medical societies which became established in Scotland from the middle of the eighteenth century onwards. They concerned themselves mostly with keeping local practitioners up to date in their professional work and sometimes it has to be said, looking after their professional interests. Secondly they were formed to provide free care for the poor. In Inverness, in 1817 the Medical Society of the North, open to all qualified practitioners, was formed to promote medical science and establish a professional library. It also published a set of rules for its members including a schedule of recommended fees which had four levels according to social class and income – two shillings and sixpence for a single consultation for the lowest class and ten shillings and sixpence for the highest In 1866 the Inverness Medical Missionary Society was started to provide free medical care for the local poor and to train medical students for missions overseas. The Inverness Medical Society was founded in 1885 to advance the educational and professional interests of local practitioners, one of its actions being to draw attention to the low level of remuneration in what it called 'club medical practice' which it regarded as contracted cheap labour.[31]

Although by the end of the 19th century such societies as outlined above in Inverness existed in most centres in Scotland, Caithness appears not to have participated. It was much later that such activity occurred in the county and this included the Highland Medical Society based in Inverness to which Caithness practitioners could belong.

All the societies mentioned so far were related to medical matters and doctors but good nursing was also a matter for concern. Nursing societies were formed but will be discussed below in association with nursing in general.

The Persistence of Folk Medicine

Towards the end of this century very definite advances were being made in medical sciences and the number of qualified doctors was increasing, but folk medicine retained its popularity and had its faithful adherents especially among the rural population.

One of the most durable of beliefs was the healing power of waters especially wells and lochs. Mary Beith mentions particularly Loch Mo Naire in Strathnaver, claiming that the majority of its users came from Caithness and that coachloads of people from the county visited up to the late 1930s.[32] The rituals associated with its use were, to say the least, dramatic and physical and mental shock may have had an effect on psychological disorders. But Caithness had its own therapeutic waters in the Loch of Hielan near Greenland. The Revd Beaton quotes Nicolson with regard to the superstitious belief of its healing powers as follows:

> Its reputation for miraculous cures died out before 1800 but persons came to the Loch of Dunnet to be cured as late as 1825 or 1830. The person who desired to be cured of an ailment had to bathe in the loch between sun and the day i.e. between daybreak and sunrise on the first Monday of a raith, (quarter) leave a silver coin in the loch and go through other forms which I have forgotten. My father, born in Dunnet in 1806, told me that he and other Dunnet boys used to search the edge of the loch after each first Monday of a raith and that he found some or saw some found.[33]

Clearly the practice had unexpected benefits!

The importance of the local 'skilly' person was also maintained. William Dun, a Latheronwheel fisherman was particularly skilled in the removal of grit or other material from people's eyes. It was said he could do this without touching the patient or even in the absence the patient![34] Perhaps his method was really that used by the mother of the child with smallpox recounted above. Another inhabitant of Latheronwheel known as Sandy Skipper's wife was believed to have particular skills with regard to children's illnesses, her therapeutic armamentarium being mainly incantations.[35] Helen Lindsay writes of cures used in Dunbeath, including boiled or fried mice for whooping-cough, rings inserted into ears for sore eyes, and burying a black cock alive to control epilepsy.[36]

A rather more credible individual was 'Doctor' John Bain of North Smerlie, Lybster, who was a self-taught herbalist, bone-setter and dentist with a reputation which extended to England and Ireland. He was a joiner by trade and never charged for his medical services. His talents did not stop there; he grew tobacco plants, made his own wine, clothes and boots and was a fiddler, a wood-carver and taxidermist of skill. He died in 1914 at the age of 88.[37]

Another curious practice was known as 'casting the lead', the following being a description of the technique:

> Following an invocation to the Trinity, some melted lead was poured into a wooden vessel containing water, which had been placed on the patient's head and if any of the solidified lead in any way resembled a heart, it was taken and turned round, with the result that 'the patient's heart returned to its place' and the disease was cured. This piece of lead was carefully preserved afterwards so as to prevent relapses.[38]

This applied particularly to insanity where the person's heart was believed to be out of its proper position. A similar practice is recorded in an article in the *John O'Groat Journal* of 1838 under the heading 'Heart casting', which claimed that 'this ingenious mode of curing disorders is not obsolete'. It reports that it was recently performed on a child at Sarclett and avers that 'no doubt can be entertained as to its efficacy'.[39]

The *'Groat'* in its early years never failed to inform its readers on health matters and carried an impressive array of advertisements for patent medicines while at the same time giving warnings against itinerant quacks. A letter to the Editor, however, recognised why people sought their help being 'deterred from calling in regular practitioners because of heavy charges'.[40] From the parish of Latheron in 1840 came a cure for strained wrist which, it was said, was often suffered by young shearers. It deserves to be recorded in full:

> Go alone at that hour when dismal ghosts complain, across a running stream that divides estates; cut nine handfuls of corn; measure the stubble ground

backwards and forwards nine times; whisk a handful of corn round your head thrice walking backwards across the stream, repeating as you scatter the corn

> Pain of joint and pain of bone
> Leave me, leave me and begone
> Pass away on midnight air
> And leave me free of pain and care.[41]

One cannot help but suspect that both the writer and the Editor had their tongues firmly placed in cheeks and that much hilarity would have been caused by anyone observed, being foolish enough to attempt the exercise!

Finally, a post-script to the practice of bloodletting. Donald McKay writing of the parish of Reay in the 1880s, emphasised how rudimentary public health measures were and how difficult was the task of sanitary inspectors. But he goes on:

> More important than all the other officials was the bloodletter. He was a man often endowed with a very sharp intelligence. He went when called many miles, and often his visitations were most successful.[42]

He names two of these men, Mr Joseph McKay of Reay and Mr Rose of Strathy. He also records the comment of another native of Reay: 'We had our own doctor, a drop of good smuggled whisky.' So much was it used that it became known as Parish of Reay's doctor.

CHAPTER SIX

The 19th Century:
The Public Health

THE REGULATION OF TRAINING of doctors and their registration went
some way to improving the care of the sick but more important by far
were the attempts to better the social conditions of the poor and badly
housed. It has long been recognised that ill-health is closely related to
poverty and nineteenth century legislation to tackle this and related
problems was of immense importance although often falling short of
the ideal.

Social and Medical Legislation

Poor law administration in Scotland depended mainly on voluntary
contributions given out in each parish. The General Assembly of the
Church of Scotland in 1818 opined that in this matter it opposed 'the
pernicious tendency of compulsory taxation'.[1] This was at a time when
large numbers were on the verge of starvation. The Parochial Boards
were under no obligation to provide medical care, and as has been
described, such care was left almost entirely to the private benevolence
of doctors and sometimes ministers. Some towns had dispensaries and
some parishes appointed medical officers.[2]

In 1845 the Poor Law (Amendment) Act created a Central Board of
Supervision in Edinburgh and made provision for parochial boards with
duties including the appointment of an Inspector of Poor, raising funds
and building or enlarging poorhouses in parishes with populations over
5,000.[3] The Inspector of Poor in country districts was later, not
infrequently the Sanitary Inspector and schoolmaster also. The Sanitary
Inspector became the right-hand man of the Medical Officer of Health.
(MOH) and with him an adviser of the local authority. A few years later
the Board of Supervision issued a circular in which it was laid down that
all poor people in need of medical attention should be seen by a
competent medical practitioner and it was further laid down that a
practitioner was not duly qualified unless he had a degree or diploma
from a university in Great Britain or Ireland legally entitled to confer

these.[4] Amelioration of the conditions of the poor was not immediate or dramatic. There was pressure on the Inspectors not to grant outdoor relief but insist on admission to the poorhouse and unlike English law Scottish poor law required a person to be disabled as well as destitute before relief was granted.[5] There was also an increase in pauper lunatics and although more were admitted to district asylums it was cheaper to keep them in the poorhouse.

The parochial boards in Caithness like boards elsewhere took on other responsibilties as time went on. In 1849, for example, Latheron Parochial Board was concerned about the appearance of cholera in the parish and that deaths from the disease had occurred at Houstry of Dunbeath. Because of this, assistance from Wick had been asked to help establish a cholera hospital at Dunbeath.[6] The Caithness boards also appointed medical officers; in 1852 Dr Robertson was described as MO to the Parochial Board of Bower and Dr Sinclair surgeon to Wick Parochial Board. (his salary was £30 per annum). In 1853 Dr Burn was MO to Latheron Parochial Board and Dr John Smith had succeeded Dr Sinclair at Wick. These and other measures were taken in Caithness against the background of a more than average degree of poverty. In 1864 there were 4–5 paupers per 100 population in the county (in 1914 it had fallen to 2–3). Individual actions of the Parochial Board were sometimes surprising. For example, the Wick Board in 1848 allowed Helen Sinclair, Bankhead, 'a sum not exceeding 30 shillings to go to the Infirmary at Edinburgh in order to get the best possible advice as regards a sore on her leg.' It was stressed however that his was not to be a precedent for the future![7]

From 1845 until the end of the century a series of acts of parliament had a cumulative effect on the health and well-being of Scots. Such diverse items of legislation as the Lunacy (Scotland) Act of 1857, the Scottish Vaccination Act 1864, the Cattle Sheds in Burghs (Scotland) Act 1866, the Scottish Public Health Act 1867, the Dairies and Milk Shops Order 1879 and the Public Health (Scotland) Act 1897, all played their part. Among these, the most important were probably the Vaccination Act which made the vaccination of infants compulsory; the 1867 Act empowered parochial boards and town councils to remove nuisances, to provide proper water supplies and drainage, to establish hospitals and was the first legislation to give any real jurisdiction in health affairs to a central department; and the 1897 act which became the principal act governing Scottish health affairs, the central authority being the Local Governnment Board for Scotland. From a purely administrative point of view the Local Government (Scotland) Act of 1889 transferred powers and duties from parochial boards to county councils and district committees and required them to appoint Medical Officers of Health (who should not engage in private practice) and Sanitary Inspectors.

The Use of Statistics

Efficient management of the public health can never be achieved without reliable figures for the prevalence of diseases, death rates and so on. In 1855 the establishment of the office of the Registrar General for Scotland made good statistics available for the first time and this date also saw the introduction of official registration of births, marriages and deaths. In 1865 death rates in Scotland were the highest ever recorded with diseases such as cholera, smallpox and typhus fever still to be feared but with numerous deaths also from typhoid fever, scarlatina, measles, whooping-cough and tuberculosis.[8]

As we have seen the situation with regard to diseases and their prevalence in Caithness at the end of the 18th and beginning of the 19th centuries (as elsewhere) was recorded by some ministers in the Statistical Account. These accounts were anecdotal and at best scrappy. The *New Statistical Account* of 1845 gave little better information but the ministers of some parishes appeared interested in health matters. For example, the Revd Charles Thomson of Wick lists the diseases most prevalent as, 'fevers, rheumatism, pleuritis, catarrh, coughs and inflamation of the throat', and he goes on to elaborate as follows:

Pulmonary consumption is not frequent amongst adults; but infants with any weakness about the chest are generally carried off in childhood by whooping-cough, which is often very general and fatal, or by different pectoral affections. Rheumatism was not common till about the beginning of the present century, when the homely warm woollen clothing of olden times began to give place to flimsier though gayer cotton dresses, which are now very generally worn. Itch is exceedingly prevalent among the children. The kind of food on which the lower orders chiefly subsist, the state of their habitations, the scantiness of their clothing, and their indifference to cleanliness, along with the contagious nature of the complaint, sufficiently account for this. Fever of a typhoid type is seldom absent from one lane or other in the burgh of Wick, Louisburgh, and Pulteneytown, whence it breaks out, and becomes epidemic in the neighbouring country. It is generally most acute soon after the close of the fishing season. Nor is it difficult to account for its severity at that period. During the fishing there are not fewer than 10,000 persons added to the ordinary population of the place; and these are necessarily crowded together, sometimes to the number of ten or twelve, in one small room. This circumstance, taken in connection with the great consumption of spirits, and the very filthy state of the houses, shores and streets, with putrescent effluvia steaming up from the fish-offals lying everywhere about, render it a wonder that typhoid diseases are not much more prevalent. The shortness of the fishing-season, the greater supply of food, and the state of excitement and activity in which all connected with the fishing live during the period of its continuance, are no doubt the great counteracting preservatives. Indigestion, arising from the almost exclusive vegetable food of the commonalty, is very frequent. The small tenants, especially the females, are perhaps most liable to this complaint; which seems to be on the increase. Small-pox is seldom long absent from the parish, and is often very fatal. Great numbers of the people have a strange antipathy to vaccination. They brand it as a tempting of Providence; whereas their rejection of this preservative is this sin. British cholera is endemic and epidemic, and often makes its appearance, especially in the latter form. It is never fatal in ordinary cicumstances. Pestilential cholera visited Wick during the fishing season of 1832, a short while after its appearance at Thurso. The number of cases reported amount to 306, of which 66 proved fatal.

He even goes on to record the proportion of sickness in the sexes at 141 females to 100 males, the proportion of sick of a degree to require medical attention as about 5–6 per cent of the population and deaths as being 20 per cent of the sick. Nor does he neglect psychiatry: 'Maniacs are very rare. Idiots and fatuous persons are remarkably common'! His interest in medicine is further demonstrated by the recording of a 'lusus naturae' (a sport of nature or freak), a child with a perfect eye on the back of the head, which lived two years. As evidence of the genuine and functional nature of this feature he says: 'It is evident it had the use of the supernumerary organ from its never allowing a cap to be kept over it'! The other ministers were less forthcoming about the health of their parishioners. In Thurso there were 'two insane, four fatuous, two blind and two deaf and dumb,' and in Canisbay the most prevalent diseases were 'fevers, inflammation and rheumatism.'[9]

The value of statistics is, of course, related to the accuracy of the information on which they are based. For example, death statistics depend on the accuracy of the death certificate and indeed on there being death certificates at all. It comes as a surprise therefore to learn that at the beginning of the period a high proportion of deaths went uncertificated (in some Highland parishes, as much as 75 per cent) and that this was a problem at the end of the century and even into the beginning of the 20th century. In his Report for 1892 the MOH. for

Caithness reported that of 440 deaths in the county, 78 were 'not certificated' or had 'no medical attendant',[10] and in 1903 he recorded 30 uncertificated deaths which included a number of young children often illegitimate. He comments , 'Not a few cases of culpable neglect contributing to the deaths of young children must pass unnoticed.'[11] That such a situation existed in our own century is now difficult to believe.

Yet, it is in the reports and statistical tables of the MOH in the 1890s that we first have a clear idea of the patterns of disease in the county. He records birth rates, death rates and the incidence of all diseases, not only the zymotic diseases (the name given then to infectious diseases) which were so common and a frequent cause of death, but also such as cancer and cardiovascular disease. The first table of births and mortality for Caithness was issued in 1891 but excluded information about the burghs of Wick and Thurso which had a separate public health organisation (Table 6). It is salutary to note the number of deaths in the under fives and that tuberculosis (phthisis) and whooping-cough were foremost of the 'grim reapers' of infectious diseases. The following year the report recorded deaths from cancer (25), diseases of the nervous system (46), cardiovascular system (47) and respiratory system (63).

That Caithness was not a particularly unhealthy population however, may be inferred from the following (probably apocryphal) anecdote. A young Edinburgh doctor in search of a practice came to the newly built town of Pulteney but finding little to do, he confided to a friend that a community who had 'tatties and herring' six times a week for dinner were immune from disease so he left in disgust for his native city.

The Infectious and Epidemic Diseases

By the 18th century some diseases such as bubonic plague were no longer causes of feared epidemics but others, such as smallpox, still took their toll of human life, although not on the same scale as previously. This century however saw the epidemic emergence in European countries of devastating disease and amongst these cholera and typhus and typhoid fevers were prominent.

Cholera

The bacillus *Vibrio cholerae*, which causes cholera, has its real home in the Indian sub-continent and other parts of the Far East but from time to time has spread in epidemics to Europe. The organism is passed by the victim in stools or vomit and the usual transmission of the disease is by infected drinking water but sometimes also by shellfish and contamination of food by flies and hands. The severe diarrhoea which is often caused, results in the loss of large amounts of water and salts from the body which is particularly dangerous in children and even today they have a mortality rate from the disease of 15 per cent.[12] Previously, and without appropriate treatment, a mortality of 60 per cent within a few hours was possible. It was sometimes referred to as 'the plague' but this was only in a sense of an epidemic or pestilence and it was in no way related to (bubonic) plague caused by the organism *Yersinia pestis* referred to above.

A huge epidemic swept Europe and reached Britain in 1831. It spread rapidly and by January 1832 was in Edinburgh and Glasgow and then to the rest of Scotland where it ultimately caused nearly ten thousand deaths. Apart from the large towns it occurred mainly among mining and fishing populations. In Caithness, 96 people died – 69 in Wick (from a total of 411 cases), 26 in Thurso and 1 in Latheron. By contrast, Ross-shire had 102 deaths and Inverness-shire 191. Sutherland, either did not make a return to the London Board of Health which compiled statistics, or had no deaths, although it is known that Helmsdale had some cases.[13] The Caithness figures cited above are probably more accurate than those in the 1845 *Statistical Account of Scotland*.

At the behest of the Privy Council a Board of Health was set up in Wick in April 1832. This was to provide medical care 'should the Cholera morbus unfortunately visit the same at the period of the Herring Fishing', a potentially dangerous situation with the influx of people into the town and the subsequent overcrowding.[14] The Board made resolutions about cleaning up the town, removing 'nuisances', setting up soup-kitchens and advocated public prayers by the clergy. The disease appeared in Thurso on 30 July and in Wick on 4 August. A temporary hospital was set up with twelve beds in the first instance; there is no record as to where this was precisely but was probably in Pultneytown. A poster (Plate 11) produced by the Board gives common sense advice in line with the current knowledge. Sobriety, 'particularly at night', certainly did no harm!

An Edinburgh doctor, familiar with Asiatic cholera was appointed with emoluments of ten shillings and six pence (10/6p) per day and the guarantee of a 'comfortable bed-chamber'. He apparently had his troubles as he resigned in six weeks. The *John O'Groat Journal* provides a clue as to the doctor's identity. In the editiion of 23 August 1844 there is reported a visit to Wick by Dr E.D. Allison, of Edinburgh, who it

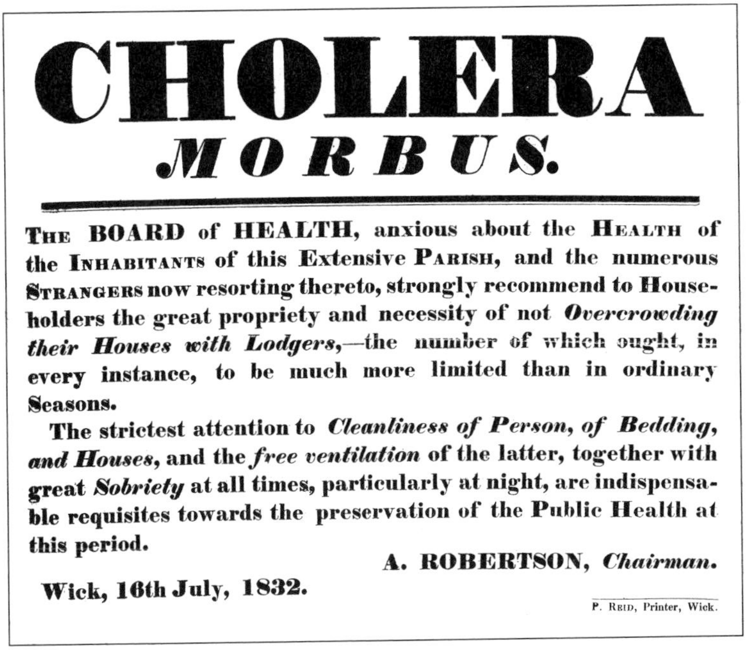

CHOLERA
MORBUS.

THE **BOARD** of **HEALTH**, anxious about the HEALTH of the INHABITANTS of this Extensive PARISH, and the numerous STRANGERS now resorting thereto, strongly recommend to House-holders the great propriety and necessity of not *Overcrowding their Houses with Lodgers*,—the number of which ought, in every instance, to be much more limited than in ordinary Seasons.

The strictest attention to *Cleanliness of Person, of Bedding, and Houses*, and the *free ventilation* of the latter, together with great *Sobriety* at all times, particularly at night, are indispensable requisites towards the preservation of the Public Health at this period.

A. ROBERTSON, *Chairman.*

Wick, 16th July, 1832.

P. REID, Printer, Wick.

Plate 11. Poster issued by the board of health in Wick, 1832, in relation to the cholera epidemic (Reproduced by permission of the Keeper of the Records of Scotland).

was said 'will be remembered in this county in consequence of his former residence here during 1832 when the cholera committed its ravages amongst us.' The article went on to say that Dr Allison was in a mood of 'forgetting and forgiving the unkind treatment he experienced' and he left a pound (£1) with the Provost for the poor![15]

The epidemic in Caithness lasted 85 days and in many repects the county was relatively fortunate as it suffered a mortality of 23.3 per cent whereas Glasgow's was 47.4 per cent. Much later in January 1834, when all was well over, the Board of Health sold off the equipment of the hospital by public roup. This was with the exception of the mattresses which were burnt but other bedding was sold after being boiled.*

Dr Venables, sent by the British Fishery Society to Pulteneytown, was one of the doctors involved in the 1832 epidemic and later wrote some comments on it in the *John O'Groat Journal.* Many of these stressed

---

*Wick was an unwitting spreader of this disease to one location. Cromarty took stringent measures to prevent its entry into the area but a Cromarty fisherman had died of cholera in Wick and although his clothes were ordered to be burned, his brother kept some of them and brought t hem home. He died of cholera which then spread amongst the other citizens.[16]

the importance of hygiene and the provision of hospital beds (at least six beds for every thousand of the population he thought sufficient). He had very modern opinions about openness and the information that should be given out by the Local Boards of Health. 'They should give due publicity to all their acts and measures,' he wrote and; 'Nothing does so much injury as mystery, or even the appearance of it.' His advice even extended to the disposal of the dead; 'The body should be wrapped up in a tarpaulin, sear cloth or painted canvas and put in a coffin pitched inside on the seams and screwed down. The sooner the internment takes place the better. It ought to be within twelve hours.'[17]

Epidemics of cholera returned to the British Isles in 1848–49, 1853–54 and 1865–66 but Scotland's and Caithness' involvement was much less than than in 1832. Nevertheless the 1832 experience was such that there was great apprehension when the disease returned and the *John O'Groat Journal* chronicled its slow but inexorable spread to Caithness. In October 1848 it reported the disease 'not beyond Edinburgh'; in November in Glasgow; in May 1849 it was in Inverness; in June, in Dundee and July in Findhorn. A letter to the Journal in October said the threat was immediate but that Drs. Sinclair, Madden and McKay were prepared. The edition of 26 October announced sombrely that cholera had arrived and had already caused several deaths – three in Bank Head and West Banks, two in Kirkhill, two in Louisburgh and one in Pulteneytown. One of those who died was a nurse attending the sick but those struck down were mainly 'the aged, debilitated and intemperate.' The editorial comment was that the Wick Parochial Board was not as efficient as the Board of Health had been in 1832. Perhaps it was constrained by the finances available; it is recorded that it had at its disposal an additional sum of £28 10s for medical purposes. Its actions during this epidemic included the provision of a soup kitchen, allowances to children whose parents had died of cholera and the engagement of five nurses who were paid £3 0s 9d[18] each. By late November 13 cases had occurred in Dunbeath with 8 fatalities. In December a total of 41 deaths in Wick was recorded and the epidemic was petering out.

The 'Return of Cholera Cases'

A record (now in private hands) and with this title was kept by one of the Wick doctors* of his cholera patients at this time. As can be seen from a sample page (Plate 12) he noted their general health and housing

*This may have been Dr Madden who in 1860 is reported to have provided a report on the recent cholera epidemic, to the Parochial Board.

RETURN OF CHOLERA CASES.

Name, Age, and Residence	*Alexander Dumand – 20 Bridge St.*
Occupation, Condition, and Habits	*Assistant to Druggist Healthful*
Description of Locality and House	*Healthful*
Date of Attack	*November 7th*
Premonitory Symptoms — Simple Diarrhœa	*Diarrhœa for 10 days*
Premonitory Symptoms — Rice Water Purging	
Cholera	*Asiatic*
Premonitory terminating in Cholera after Treatment	*he underwent no Regular treatment for the Diarrhœa*
Issue of Case	*Death in 8 hours*
Treatment	*Acetate of Lead & opium Sinapisms*
REMARKS	

Plate 12. Sample page from 'Return of Cholera Cases' (From a source in private hands).

conditions, symptoms, treatment and outcome. He dealt with a total of 54 such patients (22 adult male, 19 adult female and 13 children) between September and December, with 3 deaths. The deaths included a middle-aged nurse (probably the one mentioned in the *John O'Groat Journal*), another middle-aged woman and a 20 year old, previously healthy male assistant druggist who succumbed within eight hours, showing that the old, young, unhealthy and intemperate were not the only ones who were vulnerable. The middle-aged woman had a 12-year-old daughter who contracted the disease but recovered, and the young druggist's senior in the druggist's shop contracted the disease at the same time but recovered. Some are said to have had simple diarrhoea for only 24 hours with rapid recovery suggesting either a very mild attack of cholera (which is possible) or the patient had some other diarrhoeal disease (which is also possible) but during a cholera epidemic it is reasonable to assume it was the former. Others showed 'rice water purging' (present when severe diarrhoea gets rid of all faecal material from the gut and the result is the passage of clear fluid with flecks of mucus) and some are described as having either British or Asiatic cholera. British was described as the less severe endemic type and was possibly due to a different strain of the organism.

The treatments mentioned in these records were routine for the time. By far the commonest was a chalk and opium mixture – a palliative for diarrhoea which was used until fairly recently. Lead acetate, calomel and starch, all often combined with opium preparations and infusions of mint and bicarbonate of soda by rectum were also used and sinapisms (mustard plasters) and leeches occasionally. Some of these would give some symptomatic relief but others like blistering and leeches, could do no good and certainly some harm. The problem was that in an authorative text of 1850, no fewer than 172 cures for cholera were listed.[19] This was a reflection of the inefficacy of most of them. It is sad to consider that a really life-saving treatment, the intravenous infusion of saline, which had been shown by doctors working in Leith during the 1832–33 epidemic to be precisely that, was still not being used.[20] The technique and the results had been well publicised in the medical press but doctors all over the United Kingdom and not just in Caithness were seemingly unaware of the benefits. Today, the replacement of water and salts by intravenous infusion is the mainstay in treatment of severe cases.

The cholera epidemic of 1853–54 was not so fully recorded as the two preceding epidemics. It caused about 6,000 deaths in Scotland of which 3,892 were in Glasgow alone.[21] Little is known of its impact in Caithness.

Cholera returned to Britain for the last time in 1865 but did not appear in Scotland until 1866 and was insignificant compared with former epidemics. On this occasion Caithness escaped any involvement.

Typhus and Typhoid Fevers

'Fevers' were very common in the 19th century although at its beginning there was no general recognition of more than one kind of fever; variations in presentation were believed to depend on the circumstances in which the fever occurred. The two principal endemic fevers with a high mortality were typhus and typhoid fevers but the two were not clearly distinguished until later in the century.An indication of the confusion that existed is given in a paper on epidemic fever in Scotland in 1863–65 which listed types of fever as follows:

1) Typhus fever (also called spotted fever, low, putrid, brain and nervous fever).
2) Enteric fever (also called typhoid, gastro-enteric and gastric fever).
3) Relapsing fever (also called relapsing or short typhus and bilious typhoid fever).
4) Gastric fever (also called bilious fever)
5) Simple continued fever (also called simple typhus and simple fever).
6) Febricula – simple fever without eruption.
7) Infantile fever (also called infantile remittent fever).[22]

One of the early observations was that typhus appeared to affect the poor and wretched in particular, whereas typhoid afflicted all classes.*[23]

Typhus fever in its epidemic form is caused by an organism known as *Rickettsia (R. prowazeki)* and is transmitted by the infected faeces of the human body louse, usually through scratching the skin. The endemic form is spread by fleas which have fed on infected rats.

The severe cases in epidemics suffered sudden fever, headaches, skin rashes and became delirious and stuporous. The average mortality was between 10-20 per cent but in elderly patients could be much higher.

Typhoid fever (and together with the paratyphoid fevers are often referred to now as the enteric fevers) is caused by the organism *Salmonella typhi* and is spread by carriers of the disease or patients through contaminated food, milk or water. It is less dramatic in onset than typhus fever but produces a variety of symptoms including headache, bowel upset, cough, skin rashes and delirium. The mortality in pre-antibiotic days varied from 5–25 per cent being higher in some epidemics than others.

---

*Prince Albert died of typhoid fever in 1861!

Epidemics of typhus and relapsing fevers occurred in Scotland in 1836–9 and 1842–44 but the last considerable prevalence was in 1869–70. It was restricted mainly to a few large towns.[24] Caithness had its share of illness and deaths from this disease but never on the fearsome scale of urban areas, or indeed of the Western Isles with their insanitary black houses. At one time the MOH of Ross and Cromarty strongly recommended that every black hut infected with typhus fever should be burned down at once, his colleague in Inverness-shire taking the same view.[25] In 1894, ten cases of typhus fever were notified in Caithness and of these three died, but it is salutary to remember that as late as 1914, 56 cases of typhus were notified in Scotland all of them in the counties of Ross, Inverness and Lanark. In 1894, 14 cases of typhoid fever were notified with no deaths. The gradual improvement in sanitary conditions was bearing fruit. Nevertheless people had vivid memories of these times. Donald Grant writing in the 1960s, of Thurso in the 1890s, recalls typhoid fever breaking out in Shore Street and that Dr McLean felt compelled to report to the Board of Supervision that the town was filthy![26]

Smallpox

Despite vaccination this disease continued into the 19th century and beyond and was still one to be feared. In 1863 the Vaccination (Scotland) Act became law which made the vaccination of infants compulsory. Before this there was a continuing resistance on the part of parents to having this done. In 1838 the *John O'Groat Journal* reported that smallpox had recently been making great ravages and that several children in Pultneytown had died. It went on to deplore 'the lamentable obduracy of parents in not having children vaccinated' Furthermore it had obviously decided to add threat to persuasion in trying to rectify this by adding, 'Should we be obliged to speak again, we shall be less scrupulous about giving names'![27] By the end of the century the disease had ceased to be a significant one from the point of view of mortality but still had public health implications and importance into the twentieth century which will be referred to later.

The Medical Officers of Health

The medical men whose task it was to deal with the public health aspect of these, and other diseases had a very important role. It was recognised about the middle of the century that to improve the health of society the formation of local Boards of Health and the appointment of medical officers were necessary. The real value of the new Medical Officers of

Health lay in achieving sanitary improvements and in this respect they were at the beginning sometimes called 'medical police'. The first Scottish MOH was appointed in Edinburgh in 1862. Liverpool had appointed its first MOH in 1847.

In Caithness the burghs were first to appoint Medical Officers of Health. In 1871 Thurso appointed Dr John Grant Smith; two years later Wick appointed Dr John Alexander and the following year Pultneytown appointed Dr George Banks. These men fulfilled their public health duties on a part-time basis only but did receive a salary, Dr Banks's for example being £35 per annum. Dr Smith qualified LRCSE and LRCPE in 1854 and practised in Thurso for forty years from 1855. He was parochial medical officer for Halkirk as well as Thurso and was a certificated factory surgeon. An account of Dr Banks's career has already been given in the previous chapter.

The first full-time MOH in Caithness, Dr Alexander, was appointed in 1891. This had been discussed at the first meeting of the County District Committee of Caithness in June 1890 when the possibility of combining with the County of Sutherland to appoint a joint MOH was mooted.[28] By October 1891 this proposal had obviously been dropped but Dr John Alexander was offered the post of county MOH at a salary of £300 per annum plus £50 travelling expenses 'on condition he obtains the Diploma in Public Health at his own expense within twelve months.'[29] By 1900 he also had responsibility for the burghs of Wick and Thurso. Pultneytown however still had at the turn of the century its own MOH as befitted its independant status with a population of 5,550 as opposed to 2,962 for Wick and 3,936 for Thurso.

John Alexander. (Plate 13) was born in 1839 in the parish of Watten, his father being William Alexander of Cromquoy farm. His first intention was to become a teacher and to this end studied at Moray House Training College, Edinburgh but his interest soon turned to medicine. He qualified LRCPE, LRCSE & LM Glasgow in 1867 and practised in Northumberland showing an early interest in public health matters by becoming a certificated factory surgeon and an assistant surgeon to Bedlington Collieries. He returned to practise in Wick in 1868 and was joined there in 1875 by his younger brother Alexander, also a doctor. John, as we have seen, combined public health work in Wick with his own practice until his full-time appointment in 1891. He honoured his undertaking to obtain the Diploma in Public Health and he also became an MD of Durham University. He took his wider community responsibilities seriously, being a Justice of the Peace, a

Plate 13. Dr John Alexander (Reproduced by permission of Dr Isobel Alexander).

member of Wick Town Council and the Carnegie Public Library Committee. He supported the Liberal cause and was a faithful member of the United Free Church.[30]

His early years as MOH could not have been easy. A contemporary account of the state of sanitation in Caithness is given by Donald McKay:

> Public Health was then a very small Government baby and the laws of hygiene were not known among the crofters. The consequence was that live stock was permitted to share the meagre accommodation of the cottages with them. But though they bred thus, under circumstances which would turn the blood of a sanitary inspector cold, they seemed to thrive on this primitive mode of existence.[31]

He, Dr Alexander, had therefore to combat some very unhealthy practices but also, perhaps, the attitude that they did not really matter. His first Report to the District Committee of the County in 1891 dwelt at some length on the deficiencies and malpractices he had found and the necessity for compliance, by the local authority, with statutory enactments to deal with these. For example he wrote:

I would also impress upon the Council the great importance of adopting the 'Infectious Diseases (Notification) Act' at an early date. It will be impossible to control the spread of Contagious diseases and to prevent epidemics unless early knowledge of the first cases be obtained, so that isolation and supervision can be at once adopted – both as to those attacked and as to those exposed to infection. This matter has doubtless mixed up with it the question of Hospital accommodation which will require sooner or later to be taken into consideration. Notwithstanding however that Hospital provision in the meantime is insufficient, much benefit must accrue from the adoption of the Act. It will bring the Sanitary Officials more directly in contact with the people, and with places in an insanitary condition where disease may actually exist. Slaughter houses should be licensed and bye-laws regulating them issued. Several of these in the villages are situated too near dwelling houses; they are all defective in structure, are badly drained, without water supply and their condition generally is unsatisfactory.

Very basic requirements such as the safe handling of food, milk and water supplies came in for criticism:

Articles of food are liable to be polluted and adulterated in many ways, and in most cases it is impossible for the consumer to be protected without public intervention. The 'Food and Drugs Adulteration Act' should be adopted, and a Public Analyst appointed for the County. Milk is especially liable to contamination, and has been frequently a medium in spreading such diseases as Scarlatina, Typhoid Fever, and Consumption. Care should be taken to use the milk of cows which are abslutley healthy. Byres and the cows themselves should be kept very clean, and the dishes and the hands of the milkers scrupulously so. Milk should not be stored in sitting rooms nor in bedrooms, nor in milk houses having communication with dwelling houses, which is frequently the case throughout the County. As already mentioned, dairies and all sellers of milk in however small quantities should be registered in order that the cows and byres may be regularly inspected. No one suffering or recovering from an infectious disorder should approach the byres nor handle the milk, and any illness that may arise amongst the cows should be notified at once to the Sanitary Authorities, and the affected animals examined forthwith by a duly qualified veterinary Surgeon.

Nor did he hesitate to name places and individuals in his exposure of the unsatisfactory:

In October last I briefly reported to the District Committee on the principal villages in the County and called attention to their insanitary condition. The water supply of the villages is obtained mostly from surface wells. It is unsufficient in quantity especially during the dry months of the year and is generally liable to pollution. There is no proper drainage, no closet accommodation, and no properly constructed ashpits. The want of water is much felt at Lybster, Latheronwheel, and Scrabster, which are fishing stations, and where there is a large accession to the population for two or three months of the year. At Scrabster I am informed, by Fishcurers, Fishermen and others, that the scarcity amounted almost to a water famine on more than one occasion. I have also brought under the notice of the Local Authority the insantitary state of the small villages at Brubster and Spittal roadside. I have also reported to the Watten School Board on the School premises at Gersa, to the Reverend Mr Macpherson as to the condition of the Church of Canisbay and on complaint by the Reverend Mr Falconer as to the Church at Dunnet. I also sent a note to the tenant at Drumhead, Bower, as to the improvement of premises there.

He ended this first report with an account of the zymotic (infectious) diseases prevalent in the year and a simple table of births and mortality as shown in Table 6 opposite. From Table 6 it can be seen that influenza caused more deaths than typhoid fever and that the great killer among the infectious diseases was phthisis (tuberculosis).[32]

This first report could have been seen (and probably was) as a new broom sweeping unnecessarily clean. Nevertheless his annual reports up to his death in 1901 continued in the same frank and vigorous manner, and his desire to see the public health of Caithness improve and at least equal the best of other places shone through all his comments and actions. He travelled long distances to medical congresses and in 1900 thanked the County Council for granting 'a lengthened period of absence during which I took the opportunity of enquiring into the sanitary enactments and methods of other countries'.[33] Perhaps this was the trip which he lengthened to include a visit to his brother sheep-farming in Queensland, and to Egypt and the Pyramids.

If one man could be said to have done most to improve health in Caithness then it would be John Alexander and to their credit the people of Caithness eventually recognised this. They did this by their laudatory comments at his funeral and also by the erection of a statue and memorial to him at Riverside in Wick – a rare honour and one he well deserved.

Alexander Alexander (Plate 14) John's younger brother graduated MBCM at Edinburgh University in 1875 after attending classes in the Faculty of Arts. He immediately joined his brother in Wick but died at the early age of 45 in 1894. His death was due to one of the infectious

Table 6. Births and Mortality for 1891.

Parish	Population (Census 1891)	Total Registered Births	Illegitimate	Deaths at sub-joined ages				Deaths from Zymotic Diseases and Consumption								Death rate per 1000
				At all Ages	Under 5	5 and under 60	60 and upwards	Whooping Cough	Scarlet Fever	Measles	Dyphtheria	Erysipelas	Typhoid Fever	Influenza	Phthisis	
Bower	1,500	36	7	23	3	7	13								1	15.3
Canisbay	2,165	49	5	30	7	6	17			1					2	13.8
Dunnet	1,488	43	5	23	4	8	11	2					1		4	15.4
Halkirk	2,564	68	4	45	10	10	25	3						1	4	17.5
Keiss (quoad sacra)	1,266	34	2	24	3	7	14						1		3	19.0
Latheron	5,874	124	13	94	12	31	51	1	1				1	2	10.0	16.0
Olrig	1,833	49	6	27	5	6	16						1			14.7
Reay	1,182	24	1	13	1	2	10							1	5	11.0
Thurso (Landward)	1,824	45	8	30	6	9	15	2					1		1	16.4
Watten	1,390	33	1	15	3	4	8		1							10.8
Wick (Landward)	3,552	104	9	62	13	16	33	8	2					2	6	17.4
TOTAL FOR COUNTY	24,638	609	61	386	67	106	213	16	4	1			5	6	36	15.67

Plate 14. Dr Alexander Alexander (Reproduced by permission of Dr Isobel Alexander).

diseases which he and his brother had been battling against – typhus fever. Unlike his brother however he had a family, one of whom, his elder son, was to carry on the medical tradition.

William Alister Alexander (known affectionately to colleagues and decades of medical students at Edinburgh as 'Sandy Alexander') was born in Wick and after schooling at George Watson's College graduated in medicine at Edinburgh University in 1912. He served in the First World War in Malta, the North-West-Frontier and France, surviving the torpedoing of his troopship returning from the East.[34] After the war he lectured in morbid anatomy but then applied himself to clinical work ultimately becoming physician in charge of wards at Edinburgh Royal Infirmary in 1936. As a Fellow of the Royal College of Physicians, Edinburgh, his devoted service to it culminated in his Presidency from 1951 to 1953. He took pride also in his Presidency of the Edinburgh Caithness Society.[35] The family tradition of medicine continued with his son David and his daughter Isobel. David became Assistant Professor of Paediatrics at Queens University, Kingston Ontario and Isobel, after medical registrarship at Bruntsfield and Elsie Inglis

Hospitals, Edinburgh, became a principal in the Edinburgh University Health Service. This branch of the Alexander family did not sever all connections with its native county. A family home at Dunnet was visited regularly and Sandy Alexander took a genuine and very kind interest in the early development of Caithness General Hospital with which the writer was associated.

The remaining MOH reports until the end of the century chronicled what had been achieved but more importantly the factors which hindered further improvement. On several occasions the difficulty in dealing with 'nuisances'* was highlighted because the travelling allowance granted to the Sanitary Inspector by the Council 'was utterly inadequate for the proper execution of his work'. The same point was made with regard to the allowance for the MOH! Improvement in insanitary housing was delayed because of disputes over who was responsible for improvements. Many of the crofts were under the Crofters Commission and it was uncertain whether proprietors or tenants were responsible especially 'since land agitation has sprung up, the relation between landlord and tenant has become more strained'. The provision of hospital beds was a constant problem and even the problem of cholera had not entirely disappeared as the MOH was concerned about the difficulty in placing shipping in quarantine. No anchorage was absolutely safe in all weathers but in consultation with the Wick Harbourmaster it was agreed that Ackergill Bay would be used for the east coast and Scrabster Roads for the west.[36]

Despite all the reservation however, it is clear that most of the necessary public health measures were in place to take the county into the new century with considerable confidence.

---

*Under law, these were things 'offensive to the sight, smell or hearing of another' and generally referred to middens, dunghills and rubbish of all kinds in inappropriate places.

CHAPTER SEVEN

The Hospitals Until the National Health Service

/CAITHNESS WAS RELATIVELY LATE in acquiring anything like adequate and satisfactory hospital services. Leaving aside the mediaeval hospices, the possible leper hospitals and crude temporary buildings to cope with various epidemics, hospitals were not established in the county until late in the 19th century. In Scotland in general it was the early part of the 18th century which saw the erection of hospitals, particularly in the cities and larger towns.[1] But hospitals in smaller communities such as Ellon and Fyvie in Aberdeenshire, Kirkwall (Balfour Hospital) and Fort William (Belford Hospital) pre-dated Wick's Bignold Cottage Hospital which was opened in 1903. Perhaps this is explained by a smaller, more scattered population and the lack of individual benevolence and funding which was so important in establishing these institutions.

Although we have to conclude that most people in Caithness up to the beginning of this century suffered their illnesses and died in their own homes, some with the financial means sought treatment in hospitals elsewhere. Many would have travelled to Inverness but some went further. In 1729, the small fore-runner of Edinburgh Royal Infirmary treated thirty-five patients, one of which was Elizabeth Sinclair of Caithness.[2] She spent from 6 August to 19 November in hospital suffering from 'chlorosis' (a form of anaemia affecting especially young girls at puberty) and is reported to have been discharged 'recovered.' One hundred and fifty years later letters appeared in the local press appealing for funds for Edinburgh Royal Infirmary; in 1889 38 patients were admitted directly to the Infirmary from Caithness.[3] In the 1920s such appeals were still being well supported.[4]

There was not, however, unawareness of the need for hospitals. Sir John Sinclair writing of the parish of Thurso in the *Statistical Account of Scotland* in the 1790s said:

> The county will at all times probably have one or more educated surgeons
> by which the health of the upper ranks will be properly attended to when
> necesary. But the peasantry and servants are sometimes much neglected at

present, insomuch, that on a servant's being seized with any contagious disorder they are sometimes turned out to find quarters where best they can.

It has therefore occurred to Mr Williamson [the surgeon] that it would be advisable to have a hospital in Thurso for persons thus circumstanced; and it is proposed to have as a measure of great humanity and likely to be greatly useful, one erected by the subscriptions of the merchants in the town and the gentlemen in the neighbourhood.[5]

This, of course, never happened, but the passage is a clear indication of what hospitals were thought to be for, who they were for and how they were to be achieved.

The temporary hospitals referred to continued to be common practice in coping with epidemics well into the 19th century. We have seen that one was opened in Wick during the 1832 cholera epidemic probably in a house in Pultneytown, and Dunbeath wished to establish one in 1849. Some Parochial Boards attempted to set aside cottages for cases of casual sickness, but although the District Committee in 1895 advertised for the use of empty cottages in different districts, this was 'without practical results.'[6] One isolated act of private benevolence was the conversion by the Duke of Portland of one of the cottages at Berriedale into a hospital for the benefit of tenants and employees. This could accommodate three or four adults and had a resident nurse in charge.[7] In 1901 smallpox was very prevalent in Glasgow. This caused the local authority in Wick to erect as a precaution a temporary structure of wood and iron, (the 'prefab' or 'portacabin' of its day) on the north side of Wick river about a mile from the town. It had accommodation for six patients and one nurse but fortunately it never had to be used to deal with smallpox.[8]

Dunbar Hospital in Thurso was opened in 1883 but none of the early MOH Reports nor the hospitals section of the Medical Directories of the time make any reference to it. It is clear that it was regarded and intended as a home for the old and infirm rather than an institution for the care of the sick.[9] Its subsequent role as the latter is discussed below.

By the 1890s the more permanent hospital accommodation in existence was geared to the care of patients with infectious or zymotic diseases – rightly regarded as the most threatening of the time. Cases of infectious disease could be isolated in the Thurso area at Burnside hospital but the first MOH Report in 1891 exposed its total inadequacy. It was a wooden shack consisting of two rooms, capable of taking two adults each, and a kitchen. It was irregularly occupied and at one time had a resident nurse who was frequently doing general nursing in the town because of lack of patients in the hospital. During the year 1900 it

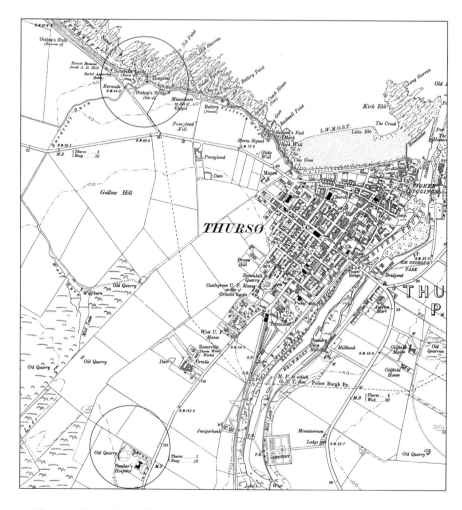

Plate 15. Map of the Thurso area (1906) showing the location of the Burnside Hospital and the Dunbar Hospital (Reproduced by Permission of the Trustees of the National Library of Scotland).

accommodated only two patients. As shown on the accompanying map (Plate 15) it was located well away from houses and seemed to be in a rather exposed position. Proposals for an improved structure ('not a large and elaborately equipped hospital')[10] had been made in 1894. Even 'a portable hospital [whatever this was] such as has been adopted by the County of Haddington would be of advantage', wrote the frustrated MOH. Plans for a twelve-bedded hospital with observation and convalescent wards were proposed and costed at £2,000. Thurso local authority could not agree to accepting this sum and even when the estimate was reduced to £1,500 no action was taken. In 1899 proposals were made to build a hospital at Georgemas to serve, in addition, Halkirk, Olrig, Watten and Bower. Tenders were not invited until 1902 and by the following year the MOH was urging abandonment of the plan and the building of a hospital in Thurso.[11] Such hospitals were never built in the Thurso or Georgemas area and the 'useless' Burnside hospital was in existence until the completion of the Town and County Hospital in Wick. It seems paradoxical that the MOH was repeatedly drawing attention to the lack of accommodation and that Burnside hospital was so infrequently used. This is, in all probablilty, explained by the natural reluctance of patients and doctors alike to make use of such poor facilities.

Wick Combination Hospital

Patients with infectious diseases in the Wick area were better served. The 'Combination' Hospital was so called because it was financed and administered by three local authorities, namely Wick Town Council, the Commissioners of Pultneytown and Caithness County Council, each providing a third of the running costs. It was situated at Harrow Park and according to the MOH was 'the only hospital in the county which is fully equipped and in regular working order.'[12] Certainly its facilities were much superior to those of Burnside hospital, boasting, as it did, two wards holding eight to nine adults, provided with baths (but without hot water!), gravitation water-supply, a mortuary, an ambulance carriage and a nurse in residence. In 1892 disinfecting apparatus was requested 'but the expense staggered the Joint Committee'! Nevertheless the MOH was still warning that if there was a severe epidemic of disease, huts or tents would have to be erected.

As evidence that this was a well-run hospital the 'Regulations for the Internal Management', first set out in 1895, may be quoted. The Chairman of the Committee was Mr William Brimms and the Clerk, Mr Daniel Sutherland. The Medical Superintendent was Dr John Alexander and the Matron, Eliza Stewart.

Visiting Physicians

The medical practitioners of the district shall act as Visiting Physicians – every patient being allowed the attendance of his or her own family doctor, and an allowance of 20s being granted for each case.

Every Visiting Physician shall visit his patient or patients in the Hospital at least once a day during the acute stage of illness, or, in cases of urgency, as often as his services may be required.

It is recommended that before visiting the wards he shall put on a coat specially reserved for the purpose, and on leaving shall take all due precautions against conveying infection from the Hospital.

He shall have full medical charge of the patients under his care, and be responsible for their treatment.

He shall enter into the ward journal the leading features of each patient's illness, and shall see that the particulars on the bed chart of each patient are carefully noted from day to day.

He shall be responsible for the ordering of all drugs and other necessaries for the patients other than food and clothing. He shall enter and initial each order in the ward journal.

Head Nurse or Matron

The Head Nurse or Matron (who must have had some experience in a Fever Hospital and be certificated) shall have charge of all domestic arrangements in the Hospital and administrative departments, and shall have control of all the ordinary nurses and domestic servants.

She shall undertake the duties of an ordinary nurse, and observe the rules laid down for her.

She shall be responsible for the cleanliness and good order of the Hospital generally, especially as regards the patients' bedding and clothing. She shall also see that the food is of good quality, properly cooked and served, and that no waste anywhere prevails.'

General Rules for the Nursing Staff

1. The Nursing Staff shall be under the directions and general control of the head Nurse or Matron, and in all matters affecting the treatment of patients they shall act by the instructions of the Medical Attendants.

2. While on duty the nurses shall wear the uniform provided for them, and must on no account enter the wards in any other dress. The uniform must not be taken or worn outside the hospital Grounds.

3. They shall be responsible for the cleanliness of the patients and wards, and shall see that quiet and good order prevail.

4. They shall accept no gratuities or presents from patients or the friends of patients.

5. They shall not see private friends in the Hospital without the sanction of the Head Nurse, and then only in the room set apart for the purpose. They shall not attempt to proselytize or interfere in any way with the religious convictions of patients.

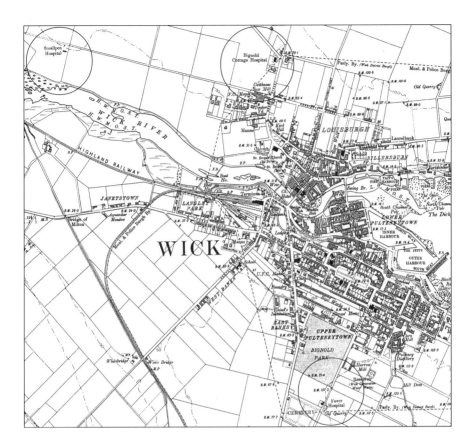

Plate 16. Map of the Wick area (1906) showing the location of the Smallpox Hospital, the Fever (Wick Combination) Hospital and Bignold Cottage Hospital (Reproduced by permission of the Trustees of the National Library of Scotland).

There were in addition Special Rules, some of which we would consider unnecessarily restrictive and detailed. For example, the matron was instructed that she would, 'go on duty at 8 am rising at 7 am and going to bed at 10 pm'! And again; 'She shall , when patients friends call to make enquiries, answer them courteously, but avoid all extraneous conversation'. As for the ordinary nurses they were to be 'on duty at such hours and for such periods as the Head Nurse may direct' and their time off duty was covered by; 'Each nurse shall be entitled to a half-holiday every week, on such days as the head nurse may deem most convenient. She shall also have a fortnight's holiday in each year.'[13]

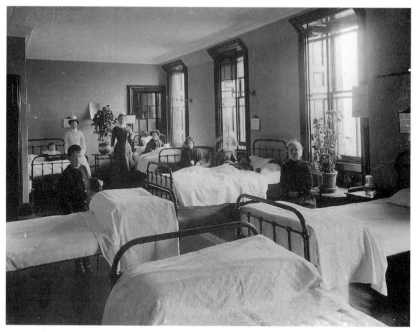

Plate 17. Ward interior Town and County Hospital, Wick (circa 1911) From the Johnston Collection. (Reproduced by permission of the Wick Society).

This hospital dealt with cases of infectious diseases prevalent at the time – typhoid fever,* scarlet fever, diphtheria, erysipelas, puerperal fever and whooping cough and did so with seemingly remarkable economy. In 1897 the average cost per patient per year was £16 19s 2d. But by the beginning of this century the deficiencies of even this hospital were becoming more obvious. In 1908 for example, the small hospital built along the Wick river at Kettleburn had to house a family removed from a house infected with typhoid fever. A map of the Wick area (Plate 16) dated 1906 shows precisely where this was and also the location of the Combination (Fever) Hospital. In 1906 a site was selected at Barnyards for a new hospital which was to function as an infectious diseases hospital for the county. Delays, which seem inherent in the building of hospitals in this country in every age, meant that it was not opened until 1910. This was the Town and County Hospital.

---

*The first entry in the admissions book is dated 7th September 1892 and concerns Elizabeth McPhee, single, a tinker of Janetstown who spent twenty-eight days in the hospital with typhoid fever.

The Town and County Hospital

The architect was Mr McDonald of Thurso and the lowest tender was
£6,361 although the eventual cost was £8,500. There was planned, a
scarlet fever pavilion of ten beds, a typhoid pavilion of 8 beds, a
diphtheria pavilion of four beds and an observation ward of one bed.
An administrative block consisted of a sitting-room and bedroom for
Matron, two day-rooms and five bedrooms for nurses, a doctor's room,
servants' rooms etc. There was to be a discharge block with offices, as
well as wash-houses, laundry, disinfecting chambers, mortuary and
ambulance shed, and all were to have the benefit of a hot water supply,
gas lighting and internal telephone. A photograph of the interior of one
of the wards shows women and children together in a light, airy, well-
ordered environment and neatly dressed efficient-looking nurses. (Plate
17)

The formal opening of the hospital took place on 13 September 1910
and was carried out by the Right Honourable John Sinclair, Baron
Pentland of Lyth who at that time was a member of the Government as
Secretary for Scotland.*[14] The first meeting of the directors of the new
hospital did not take place until early the following year with ex-
convenor Nicholson in the chair. Staff appointments were made
including Miss McGillivray as matron at a salary of £45 per annum plus
board and uniform. The nurses' salary was £28 30s per annum and the
probationers' was £12 per annum. It was decided to appoint one medical
officer to attend all cases and Dr W.P. Cormack was selected and
awarded a salary of £40 per annum. He had been in practice in Wick
since 1904, having graduated in Edinburgh in 1900 and been a ship's
surgeon with the Bibby Line. The County MOH acted as Medical
Superintendent. At the same meeting discussion took place whether to
sell or let the old Harrow Park Hospital.

In the opening year the hospital dealt with one case of erysipelas, four
of diphtheria, 40 of scarlet fever and 35 of enteric fever with only two
deaths. The arrangement whereby one practitioner attended to all
patients in hospital with one matron one nurse and one probationer
appeared to be working well although other nurses had to be employed
from time to time.[15] It was with obvious pride that the MOH report for
the same year recorded the purchase for £486 11s 6d of the first motor

---

*Lord Pentland had a busy day in Wick, as advantage was taken of his presence
to invite him to unveil the statue of Dr John Alexander. This was followed by
a cake and wine banquet in the Town Hall.

ambulance. It had a 14–16 HP engine, pneumatic tyres and an Argyll body similar to that of the ambulance of Ruchill Hospital, Glasgow.

Until the arrival of the National Health Service the hospital continued to deal with the County's infectious diseases problems although as the century advanced the incidence and severity of many of these diminished.

An exception to this was tuberculosis the successful control of which did not begin until after the Second World War.

This war brought tragedy to the hospital. On 26 April 1941 an RAF Whitley bomber from the Wick station crashed onto the administrative block which was destroyed. Two of the hospital's maids were killed as well as the crew of the aircraft.[16] Fifty-five years later this event was commemorated by the unveiling of a plaque outside the entrance to the hospital. Relatives of the two young maids (Miss Joan Bain and Miss Mary Watters) were present as well as relatives of the six RAF men who died – all from 612 (County of Aberdeen) Squadron.[17]

The Dunbar Hospital

Alexander Dunbar of Scrabster was a Deputy Lieutenant of the county of Caithness who is described as a lessee of the Bishopric of Caithness and tacksman of the Crown lands. At his death in 1859 his will directed that the whole of his estate, worth £9,737, be held and accumulated until it was sufficient to build and maintain a hospital. This hospital (perhaps more correctly called Dunbar's Hospital) was intended for the care of the sick and for the care of 12 elderly infirm people who could not support themselves financially. Dunbar was quite specific in many of his intentions, for example;

> In all cases those labouring under and suffering from any incurable disease are to be preferred. My desire is that the hospital and the dwellings for the aged persons be built in the town or the vicinity of Thurso, and that the inhabitants of that parish be preferred for admission in either department of it, and that therafter the inhabitants of the county of Caithness be preferred, and that natives of the town and county have a preference over strangers.[18]

He obviously did not think that it was a matter of urgency as he directed that the funds be allowed to accumulate for at least forty years! In 1880 however, an Act of Parliament (Accumulation Act) ruled that no trust funds could accumulate for more than twenty-one years from the death of the donor. By this time the funds had reached £18,500 and the executors had to act.

The present site of the hospital was feued from one of the trustees, Sir Tollemache Sinclair, and plans were prepared by Edinburgh architects. The cost of the hospital itself was £3,393 and of the associated cottages, £800.

The Hospital in Existence

Thurso Town Council took advantage of a visit to Caithness by HRH. the Duke of Edinburgh, (Prince Alfred, Queen Victoria's fourth child and second son) who was staying at Ackergill Tower, to create a Royal occasion. The Prince readily agreed to visit Thurso and lay the foundation stone which he did on 21 January 1882.* The short notice of the visit was blamed for a poor turn-out of the Queen's loyal subjects.

Permission was granted to name one of the wards 'Albert' or 'Edinburgh'. (It is not clear which was used), and the hospital was in use by 1883 and the cottages by 1885. (Plate 18)

How the hospital functioned in its early days is not certain. From its inception up to 1920 it was run on a day to day basis by a 'keeper' and a

Plate 18. Dunbar Hospital, Thurso (circa 1885) (Reproduced by courtesy of Mr M. Luciani).

---

*This contained the usual sealed bottle containing copies of local newspapers, coins of the realm and a copy of Alexander Dunbar's will. The building itself has been described as 'quiet baronial'.

'matron'. In other small hospitals in the nineteenth century 'keeper and matron' often implied a married couple in residence, with appropriately designated duties but there is nothing to confirm that this was the case at the Dunbar. There were seldom more than half-a-dozen inmates at a time and as has been mentioned above it was regarded as a home for the aged and infirm rather than a hospital. In 1920 it is recorded that a fully trained nurse, Miss Marr, was appointed matron the implication being that before then the incumbents were not trained nurses. Miss Marr was to occupy this post for 27 years.

In 1924 the hospital was in a perilous financial state and the Court of Session in Edinburgh was petitioned to allow other sources of money to be tapped. The local branch of the Red Cross Association agreed to hand over funds (ultimately amounting to £1,032) provided changes could be made to the management and function of the institution to allow its use as a true cottage hospital for the benefit of the surrounding district. All these changes came about and in 1925 the first meeting of the reconstituted Management Trust took place. The Trust now consisted of ten appointees – three acting under the Deed of Trust of Alexander Dunbar, two elected by subscribers and one each from the Scottish Board of Health, Thurso Town Council, the Parish Council of Thurso, Caithness County Council and Caithness Education Authority. Its first Chairman was Col D. Keith Murray who served until the inception of the NHS in 1948. Local subscribers responded generously and this allowed, in the late 1920s, structural alterations and additions to be made to the buildings, electric light to be installed and X-ray apparatus to be bought. In 1931, a surgeon was appointed to the county and all this transformed the use of hospital, undeniably for the better.

Further Landmarks

1936 saw important extensions to the hospital including a large children's ward, two private rooms and a surgeon's room. These had been planned by the Thurso architect, Sinclair MacDonald, who died before their completion. His son Hugh MacDonald carried it on. Recognising that the hospital could not function properly without an ambulance, Thurso Townswomen's Guild rolled up its sleeves and raised the necessary funds. The result was a splendid 18 horse power Austin! The Guild added to the occasion of the opening of these important extensions in August 1936 by organising a fund-raising fete in the grounds of the hospital, luckily on a day of brilliant sunshine. The formal opening was carried out by Sir Archibald Sinclair, Bart, MP who was accompanied by Lady Sinclair, their daughters Catherine and Elizabeth and young son Robin. Lady Sinclair in paying tribute to the hospital said that it was 'not only the most up-to-date, scientific hospital north of Aberdeen, (a claim that might have been disputed by Inverness) but the most kindly hospital in Scotland.'[19]

In addition to the surgeon the 1930s saw the appointment of a 'masseur' (physiotherapist) and the day-to-day work was carried out by the matron, four sisters, seven probationers, a cook and domestic staff and a caretaker who also drove the ambulance. In 1933, an average year, 245 patients were admitted (176 surgical, 61 medical and 5 maternity) and 235 were seen as out-patients. 114 X-ray examinations were made. The running cost for all this was £1,645.

The Dunbar continued a similar role until the inception of the NHS in 1948.

The Bignold Hospital

This was the first hospital in Caithness not devoted exclusively either to those suffering from infectious diseases or to the elderly infirm. Although not opened until 1903 it was conceived when thought was being given in 1897 to the best way of celebrating Queen Victoria's Diamond Jubilee in Wick.

A committee formed to raise finds succeeded in collecting £249 3s 1d, a sum recognised as totally inadequate for the purpose and it was not until Mr (later Sir) Arthur Bignold, Member of Parliament for the Northern Burghs bought Northcote House in 1901 and gifted it to the town as a cottage hospital that the matter progressed. The Diamond Jubilee Cottage Hospital Committee agreed to hand over its funds to the Bignold Cottage Hospital Committee and this act prompted the release of other monies to the project. The Dr Alexander Alexander Memorial Fund handed over £200 (provided one of the wards was named the Alexander Memorial Ward), the trustees of Miss Janet Wares contributed £480 and the trustees of Mr Alexander Bain added £75. With other donations in kind (for example Messrs McEwan, house furnishers, Wick, furnished one of the wards at their own expense) the hospital became a reality.

The building, as has been said, was Northcote House altered and extended. It boasted a lift to take stretcher cases to the upper floor where the wards – one male, one female, two small private rooms (a total of ten beds) and an observation room – were originally situated. The new operating room was lined with glass slab and was floored with white tiles. There was a convalescents' sitting- room, matron's room, kitchens and other service rooms. The management was in the hands of a Board of Trustees consisting of the oldest ordained ministers in Wick of the Church of Scotland, the United Free Church of Scotland and the Free Church of Scotland together with the Provost of Wick, two representatives elected annually by Wick Town Council, one member of Caithness County Council and one of Wick Parish Council. The Medical Superintendent was the MOH Dr Dick and the first Medical Officer recorded was Dr Elliot although later the general practitioners of Wick became honorary medical staff. The first Matron was Miss Paterson who had been a member of the Queen Victoria Jubilee Nursing Association in Wick.

The opening ceremony on the 13th July 1903 was carried out by Sir Felix Simon FRCP in the presence of Mr Bignold, Sir Keith Fraser and a host of local dignitaries. During the course of the addresses it was stated that the purpose of the hospital was 'doing good to the poorer inhabitants of Caithness and more particularly the Royal Burgh of Wick' and also (by Sir Keith Fraser) that, 'It really seems incredible that in the twentieth century in such an important town as Wick, which has been connected for half a century by railway with the South, that hitherto it has been without a hospital.' But even this criticism failed to mar the occasion which was celebrated in rhyme by Mr George Levack as follows:

To sooth the woes of human-kind,
Declares a true and godlike mind,
For this is Heaven's eternal plan,
To prove the unity of man,
For man to man is still allied
No matter where he doth reside.
This hospital will stand for years,
A place to sooth life's woes and fears.
To aid the widow in distress,
When trials great upon her press,
Such gifts as these are still designed
To sooth the ills of human kind,
And make the name of Bignold shine

For acts beneficent, benign.
We praise him then, though much extoll'd,
Such gifts as these are more than gold.
To aid the widow in distress,

To help the poor and fatherless,
These are true Liberals ever still,
Who doth the end of life fulfill,
Not in their words but in their deeds,
Relieving suffering human needs.
A solace to their fellow man,
By carrying out high Heaven's plan.
These are true Liberals ever still,
And all the ends of life fulfill,
For he who lives for self alone
Hath not the name of Liberal known.[20]

Although Sir Arthur Bignold had donated around £6,000 in purchasing, altering and equiping the building he continued his generosity by giving £300 per year towards running costs. By 1910 the average annual maintenance was £500 but this was the year Bignold lost his seat and his annual donation was not continued. This precipitated a crisis and the Trustees exhorted the public to increase its support because if it did not the consequence would be the use of capital and eventual closure of the hospital. The people of Caithness were urged to support the Bignold rather than outside county charities such as the Edinburgh Royal Infirmary.[21] The response was satisfactory and by 1916 there was an excess of ordinary income over ordinary expenditure of £117 7s 0d.[22]

From then until the 1930s the financial position remained on the whole satisfactory. In 1931 the capital account contained £25,366 and the revenue account showed a surplus of income over expenditure of £109. The custom of endowing beds helped greatly and donations large and small and in kind were always forthcoming. In 1919 Sir R.L. Harmsworth donated 1,000 shares in the Wick and Lybster Light Railway Company and every year people had their names recorded who had made gifts under the headings: magazines, butter and eggs, fowls, game and meat, potatoes and turnips, flowers, fruit and vegetables, oatmeal, fish, and miscellaneous.

The Early Workload

In the first years the average number of patients dealt with was 60 per year (in 1908 there were 62 of whom 11 had suffered accidents). The activity of the hospital had increased greatly by 1916 when there were 197 on the register of cases, 71 of which were day patients undergoing minor surgery. Only 37 had medical as opposed to surgical conditions. A page from the abstract of the register (Plate 19) gives some idea of the

ABSTRACT FROM REGISTER OF CASES, 1916.

Disease.	Age.	Sex.	Treatment.	Result.	Days in Hospital
1 Abscess	65	M	Abscess opened	Good	17
2 Acute rheumatism	32	M	Medical treatment	Good	39
3 Appendicitis	12	M	Medical treatment	Good	24
4 Gastric ulcer	37	M	Medical treatment	Good	29
5 Mastitis	39	F	Medical treatment	Good	2
6 Hernia	7	M	Radical cure	Good	20
7 Hernia	56	M	Radical cure	Good	30
8 Varicose veins	59	F	Medical treatment	Good	26
9 Mastoid abscess	7	M	Abscess opened	Good	26
10 High myopia	34	M	Paracentesis of anterior chamber	Good	9
11 Hæmorrhoids	42	M	Ligatured	Good	17
12 Hæmorrhoids	16	M	Ligatured	Good	4
13 Hernia	25	M	Radical cure	Good	25
14 Stricture	34	M	Dilated	Good	10
15 Fractured ribs	34	M	Rest and strapping	Good	22
16 Enlar. turbinated bones	15	M	Bones removed	Good	1
17 Leucoma of cornea	9	F	Subconjunctival injection	Good	1
18 Abscess	61	M	Abscess opened	Good	37
19 Fractured femur and humerus	8	M	Surgical treatment	Good	52
20 Strabismus	3	M	Tenotomy of internal rectus	Good	1
21 Hernia	11m.	M	Radical cure	Good	1
22 Appendicitis	12	M	Appendix removed	Good	29
23 Scirrhus of breast	47	F	Radical excision	Good	29
24 Sprained knee	32	M	Surgical treatment	Good	11
25 Hydrocele	60	M	Excision	Good	11
26 Malignant tumour of thigh	68	F	Excised	Good	15
27 Double ovaritis	56	F	Double ovariotomy	Good	35
28 Influenza	10	M	Medical treatment	Good	10
29 Gallstones	30	F	Medical treatment	Good	12
30 Tonsilitis	31	M	Medical treatment	Good	7
31 Myopia	34	M	Paracentesis of anterior chamber	Good	5
32 Chronic osteomyelitis of toe	10	M	Amputation	Good	12
33 Caries of Ulna	5	M	Curetted and cauterised	Good	2
34 Verruca of nose	8	F	Excised	Good	1
35 Stricture	22	M	Slit up	Good	19
36 Sprained ankle	26	M	Rest and strapping	Good	13
37 Suppurating thumb	32	M	Opened and drained	Good	1
38 Abscess in groin	10	F	Opened and drained	Good	1
39 Tubercular glands in neck	12	F	Excised	Good	3
40 Intestinal catarrh	22	M	Medical treatment	Good	9
41 Gastric ulcer	26	F	Medical treatment	Good	28
42 Chronic ulceration of leg	31	F	Amputation	Good	29

Plate 19. Page from the Register of Cases, Bignold Hospital, 1916 (Reproduced by permission of the Archivist, The Highland Council).

diseases dealt with. The surgery in the first years was carried out principally by Dr Elliott and a list of the conditions he tackled and the procedures he carried out shows the width of his experience. In 1903 and 1904, for example, he dealt with the following: ovarian dermoid cyst – opened and drained; chronic rheumatism – limbs straightened under chloroform; cataract – removed; strangulated hernia – operation; injury to arm – skin grafting; TB glands – excision; compound fracture both legs – screwed; and so on.[23]

The war years from 1914 to 1918 provided additional strains on the hospital and staff. For one thing the Medical Superintendant Dr Dick was serving in the RAMC in France and of the five honorary medical officers (Drs Banks, Rae, Kennedy, Leask and Wright) one, – Dr Kennedy was serving in the RAMC in Egypt. Moreover, in addition to civilian cases, service men from the Royal Navy were also treated. By 1918, X-ray apparatus had been gifted by the Misses Henderson of Rosebank and in 1919 66 X-ray examinations were made. In the same year the hospital admitted 119 patients of whom only 13 were medical; 81 operations were performed not including 36 minor out-patient operations.

One service man from the Royal Navy who was *not* treated in the Bignold Hospital was Prince Albert (the future King George VI) who was serving as a midshipman at this time, but his illness must have caused a little flutter within the Wick medical community. Only three weeks after the onset of the war, Sir James Reid, Physician-in-Ordinary to the King was asked to go at once to Wick where the Prince, who had appendicitis, was to be landed from HMS *Collingwood*. Reid saw the Prince with the Fleet Surgeon on the hospital ship *Rohilla* when it was decided it was not safe to move him ashore. The *Rohilla* sailed for Scapa Flow, escorted from Wick Bay by two destroyers, and then to Aberdeen where the Prince had his appendix removed by Professor Marnoch, the professor of surgery.[24]

The 1928 Extension

A few years later it was becoming evident that the 11 beds available were inadequate for the workload which had developed. An extension to the hospital had become imperative and happily this was achieved in 1928. This was a T-shaped building to the south of the old hospital consisting of two public wards with 10 beds each and two private wards with 2 beds each. A new operating room (Plate 20) with an anaesthetising and sterilising annexe was added, the cost of which was defrayed by Lt. Col.

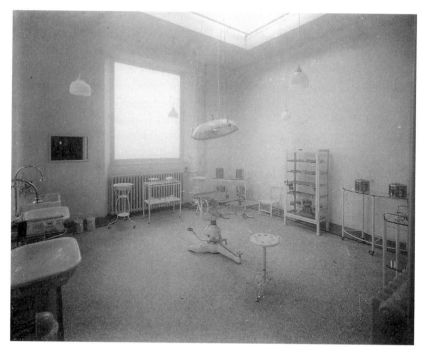

Plate 20. Operating Room, Bignold Hospital, circa 1928 (From the Johnston Collection. Reproduced by permission of the Wick Society).

Waters. The sum of £6,330 was donated by Miss Barbara Davidson to whom the female ward was dedicated. The other ward was dedicated to the memory of Mrs Evelyn Flett. Electricity now lit the entire hospital. Despite this financial support a special appeal had to be launched to cover the debt of the new extension particularly with regard to replacing the X-ray apparatus.[25]

The extension to the hospital obviously increased the clinical activity and this, with the advances in medical and surgical practice and the increase in specialisation made the appointment of specialists, particularly in surgery, a necessity. The first surgical specialist appointed in Caithness was Mr Sydney G. Davidson FRCS in 1931, who was followed in 1934 by Mr G. A. Mitchell, both on three year contracts. In 1937 Mr A.N. Roxburgh FRCS was appointed and served as the county surgeon until his retirement in 1967. These appointments were made by the Highland and Islands Medical Board.

Second World War Problems

When, in 1939, war yet again shadowed the land, the hospital was in a better position to cope with the demands made on it than in 1914, but the demands proved to be much greater. Caithness men and women once again departed to serve on many fronts but this time towns came under direct enemy attack and there was a great influx of civilian and service personnel. British and Polish troops were stationed in the county as well as many Royal Air Force men. Later in the war a German POW camp housing some 1600 prisoners was established at Watten. The population of Wick itself expanded to some 20,000 people.

To meet these various and potentially dangerous circumstances plans had to be made. Late in 1939 plans were approved for the erection of a wooden hut at the front of the hospital for the reception of casualties and for the widening of the side entrance to avoid congestion in the event of large numbers of casualties.[26] A large trench was dug in the hospital grounds as an air-raid shelter.[27] That the stresses on the hospital and its staff were real can be seen from the February 1940 admission book when in one night 20 merchant seamen suffering from exposure, burns and fractures were admitted. This was in addition to airmen from the RAF station.[28] In May 1940 a special meeting of the trustees was convened to discuss a unanimous view of the county air raid precautions (ARP) committee that hospital accommodation with operative facilities should be provided elsewhere than at the Bignold. This, of course, was to cope with the possibility of large numbers of air raid casualties and the ARP Committee had recommended that Lybster Higher Grade School be used for this purpose. Dr Dick had to remind the Trustees that the Bignold Hospital was a designated First-Aid Post and therefore would have to be maintained in some form. There was unanimity that representation should be made to the Department of Health that the hospital be evacuated to Lybster leaving only equipment necessary for a First-Aid Post, although Colonel Horne urged that the action be taken then without waiting for Department approval which he thought (probably correctly) would be bureaucratically delayed.

Only two months later Wick suffered its first air attack. Fifteen people were killed and twenty-two injured. In coping with these the hospital staff was helped by the local medical practitioners and lady volunteers from the community who were trained nurses.[29] On 24 October the Luftwaffe struck again leaving three killed and thirteen injured. This time the hospital itself suffered damage to windows, doors and ceilings.

The following day, which was a Sunday, the Trustees met to give urgent thought to what had been discussed since May, namely, the evacuation of the hospital to Lybster. The medical presence, namely Dr Dick, Mr Roxburgh and Dr McFarlane of the Department of Health, were unanimous that the hospital should be evacuated at once to Lybster and that the only remaining function in Wick should be that of casualty clearing station and first-aid post.[30] The move was carried out and from then until 1945 the Bignold functioned at Lybster. Nevertheless the Department of Health was insisting on keeping more than first-aid facilities at Wick and in a letter to the Trustees the Secretary of State stated it was 'essential to keep Bignold Hospital open and available, ready to function as a hospital of 15 beds…Under these proposals Lybster Hospital cannot be regarded solely as a hospital limited in general to the treatment of acute surgical and medical cases but will most probably have to treat in addition other types of cases, eg. military sick.'[31]

At Lybster forty-four beds were available and this necessitated, for the first time in Caithness, the appointment of junior hospital staff. Dr Douglas Aitken was appointed but before he could take up his post he was called up. The first incumbent of the resident house officer post was Dr James Miller, an Edinburgh graduate, whose salary was £175 per annum and who was provided with accommodation at the Portland Arms Hotel.[32] Later, a Mr Butler was appointed at a salary of £50 per annum plus board and travelling expenses with accommodation arranged at Forse House.[33] One can only conclude that no qualified medical people were available then and that this was a medical student.

Miss May Sutherland who had her nursing and midwifery training at Edinburgh Royal Infirmary and the Simpson Maternity Hospital, and who later became Matron of the Bignold and Central Hospitals, came as a staff nurse to the Bignold Hospital at Lybster in 1943. She recounts that it was the science laboratory at the school which became the operating theatre and that the gymnasium had emergency beds for the possibility of large numbers of civilian or service casualties, but fortunately never had to be used. She remembers also the strains under which all had to work; nurses frequently worked twelve hours a day for seven days a week and at one period she did this for six weeks at a stretch.[34]

It was, of course, the Lybster hospital that dealt with the only survivor – the rear gunner – of the air crash near Cnoc Dun, a mile north of Braemore Falls, which killed the Duke of Kent in August 1942 and in which a total of fifteen perished.

The Bignold and the RAF

The Wick Bignold Hospital was not however allowed to lie fallow. As part of the ARP facilities a gas cleansing station was built there and in 1941 it was agreed that medical orderlies from the RAF would be on stand-by duties there during air-raids as the staff at the hospital consisted of 'only three young girls.'[35] A few RAF men were also billeted at the hospital.

The RAF had a major service component in the county with aerodromes at Wick, Skitten, Castletown and Dounreay. The Wick station was under Coastal Command and Caithnesians saw an impressive range of aircraft operating from these fields – Ansons, Skuas, Hurricans, Spitfires, Grumans, Hudsons, Whitleys, Wellingtons, Hampdens, Beaufighters and others. It is not surprising therefore that RAF need for hospital accommodation was great. Although Forse House was used as an auxillary hospital for service personnel, the RAF as its activities grew, needed more at Wick.

In January 1943 Dr Dick had meetings with the senior medical officers of the RAF Medical Branch at Wick concerning the possible erection of a hospital in or near Wick aerodrome. Other options were an RAF Hospital to be built within the Bignold Hospital grounds with collaboration between the two and the handing over of the Bignold to the RAF for the duration of the war. Three months later the Air Ministry wrote to the Trustees seeking 'approval for the transfer of Bignold Hospital to the RAF until further notice.'[36] This the Trustees were unable to give without adequate compensation and certain promises and after further consultation with the Department of Health for Scotland, these were eventually agreed to. On 24 June 1943 the Trustees under the chairmanship of Commander Gore-Browne-Henderson finalised the hand-over which implied among other things, the conversion by the Ministry of the electricity supply from DC to AC and the payment by the Ministry of rents, rates and insurances. It also agreed to provide nursing help for out-patient clinics at the hospital, freeing trained nurses resident at the Bignold to work at Lybster.[37]

This, then, was the position until the end of the war. Reversion to normality did not take place automatically and not as quickly as the Trustees thought it should have. In May 1945 not long after VE Day they were making strong representations to the Air Ministry for the release of the Bignold Hospital although they thanked the RAF for the facilities offered for the treatment of civilians at Wick. The tenancy of Lybster school was finally relinquished on 3 December 1945.[38]

Plate 21. Miss Adelaine Florence Henderson (From 'Times Gone Bye', North of Scotland Newspapers Ltd).

From the end of the war there were only three years until the inception of the National Health Service. Things quickly reverted to the more tranquil routines of peace-time although it is with surprise that we learn that in 1946 the staff was complaining to the RAF about the disruption caused by low-flying aircraft (apparently Polish pilots were the main culprits).[39] But the humdrum tasks of hospital management went on – finding money for a new ambulance (the Department of Health unwilling to give a grant) and buying a cardiograph (this cost £200) – until the task of the Trustees in running a voluntary hospital came to an end. At their last meeting on the 3rd July 1948 it was resolved to insert a notice in the *John O'Groat Journal* thanking the public for its generous support since the hospital's origins.[40]

The Henderson Memorial Nursing Home

Miss Adelaine Florence Henderson of Rosebank (Plate 21) was for many years an Honorary President of the Wick and Pultneytown District Nursing Association. She was also a very generous financial supporter and her beneficence persisted after her death in 1927. To the Association she left in her will the house (Plate 22) and money:

Plate 22. The Henderson Memorial Nursing Home. From the Johnston Collection (Reproduced by permission of the Wick Society).

for the purpose of establishing, equipping and partially endowing a nursing home to be known as 'The Henderson Memorial Nursing Home' in memory of her sisters and herself. She desired that the said nursing home should be established for the treatment of patients usually resident in the County of Caithness who are willing to pay such charges for nursing and board as would, coupled by the help thus given by her, produce a revenue sufficient to meet the expenditure of said Nursing Home.[41]

In a booklet about the Home published in the early 1930s the ambience which was aimed at was admirably set out:

'...the staff are most anxious to provide a home-like feeling at Rosebank. This desire is to make it a pleasant home where people who are worn-out or indisposed might possibly avoid serious illness by coming to it for a week of quiet rest.'[42]

She had also presented to the police department of the County of Caithness a motor ambulance, appropriately named the 'Rosebank Ambulance.' (Plate 23) In her will she left a further sum of £2,000 for its upkeep and requested that it should be housed in the garage she had built for it at Rosebank.

Plate 23. The 'Rosebank' ambulance. From the Johnston Collection (Reproduced by permission of the Wick Society).

The Association was at first reluctant to accept the legacy without further consideration. It remitted the matter to a special committee which met with Miss Henderson's trustees who informed it that the legacy could not accumulate indefinitely but that there was no limit as regards the nature of the nursing home and that a portion of the grounds could be feued.[43] Following a statement from architects about necessary alterations in the house, estimates of furnishing and equipping and the cost of staff, it was calculated that only about £120 per annum would be left for food, drugs and upkeep, a sum that was considered quite inadequate. A request was made to Miss Henderson's trustees to augment the legacy but this was rejected.[44] The committee then met with the doctors in the town who suggested that an approach be made to public bodies with regard to grants being obtained for maternity work.[45]

The committee was now calling itself 'the Rosebank Committee' and was under pressure from the Town Council and the Ratepayers Association to accept Rosebank. It was not until May 1928 that the committee voted (it was a majority, not a unanimous vote) to do so. A further two years went by and the repairs and alterations were able to be carried out from the income from capital for the three years that the house was unoccupied.

The opening took place on 13 August 1931 with the ceremony being performed by Mrs Kenneth Duff-Dunbar of Hempriggs. Tea was taken on the lawn in bright sunshine and indoors Mrs G. Duff-Dunbar of Ackergill Tower unveiled a portrait of the late Miss Henderson. Provost Duchart welcomed the institution as a nursing, convalescent[46] and maternity home and as complementing the other two hospitals in the town. The company then inspected the premises and admired the alterations including the newly installed electric light, bathrooms etc. It was thought the charges were very reasonable being three guineas per week for a private ward and one guinea per week for the other wards.

The first matron was Miss Begg and she, with the trustees and the management committee ran a very successful operation until 1948 and the introduction of the NHS. At the committee's last meeting on the 11 June 1948 it was recorded with pleasure that one of it's nominees, Mr John Harper, had been appointed as one of the members of the Board of Management of the Caithness Group of Hospitals. It is a pity, however that a somewhat discordant note appeared in the proceedings. Miss Begg brought to the Committee's attention that according to the appropriate scale she should be paid at the rate of £320 per annum whereas she was being paid at the rate of £280 per annum. The Treasurer objected to paying the increase without official notification and 'he categorically refused to do anything about the increase. The Committee had no choice but accept Mr Millikens decision.'[47]

The Medical Staffing of Hospitals

It is clear from the foregoing that patients admitted to the hospitals in Caithness in the 19th and early 20th centuries were looked after by the practitioners of the area. These men were true generalists using the (by present standards) limited therapeutic armamentarium of the time but also performing with skill a range of routine surgical operations. The first Medical Officers of Health acted as Medical Superintendents but it was in 1910 in relation to the Town and County Hospital that the principle of each practitioner looking after his own patients in hospital was modified. Dr W.P. Cormack was appointed to attend all admissions to this hospital but he himself was a practitioner in town.

As the century advanced and as medical science advanced with it the need for more detailed knowledge and experience of some aspect of medicine, that is, specialisation, became apparent. When, in 1914, arrangements for a Caithness Sanatorium to deal with tuberculosis were being discussed it was recognised that a specialist physician was essential and that neither the MOH nor a local general practitioner could be appointed.[48] In 1936 at a meeting of Caithness County Council Dr Dick, the MOH said that the local medical profession agreed that the appointment of a medical consultant was desirable.[49] The following year thought was being given to providing a salary for such an appointee but this appointment was not to be made for another 27 years!

The first specialist appointment to Caithness hospitals was, not surprisingly, in the discipline of general surgery and was made in 1931. This appointment and those others made up to 1948 were under the auspices of the Highlands and Islands Medical Board. The first incumbent was Mr Davidson.

Sydney Gordon Davidson took his MA degree at Aberdeen University in 1920 and qualified MBChB in 1924. He became a Fellow of the Royal College of Surgeons of England in 1930 and of the Edinburgh College in 1987. He was on a three year contract to the Caithness hospitals and his main base was the Bignold hospital but by 1931 there were surgical facilities also at Dunbar hospital. He returned to Aberdeen where he became surgeon to the Royal Infirmary as well as to the Royal Aberdeen Hospital for Sick Children and at Woodend. He was followed by Mr Mitchell.

George Archibald Grant Mitchell, OBE, TD, qualified MBChB (Hons) in 1929 and thereafter acquired the degree of Master of Surgery (Ch.M.) of Aberdeen, DSc of Aberdeen and MSc of Manchester. He had a distinguished academic and war-time career, becoming professor of anatomy at Manchester and subsequently dean of the medical school there. During the 1939-45 War he was officer commanding a surgical division in the Middle East Forces and adviser in penicillin to the 21st Army Group. He was author of textbooks on anatomy.

In 1937 Mr Roxburgh was appointed and by the time of his retirement in 1967 was (and still is) the longest serving specialist and consultant in Caithness. The major part of his unique record of service was, however, as a consultant surgeon in the NHS and this will be described in Chapter 10.

A very necessary colleague of the surgeon is the anaesthetist, and all three of these surgeons were ably served by general practitioner anaesthetists. However, anaesthetics in the county did not start with the specialist surgeons (any more than did surgery for that matter) and many of the general practitioner surgeons must have given their own anaesthetics if a colleague was not at hand. It may be surprising to some how far back this practice goes. In 1848 the *'Groat'* reported with some excitement the 'application of chloroform in Wick!' Dr Sinclair was recorded as having removed a large growth from the side of the lip of a man from Wester. The patient happily confirmed that he had 'no more pain than the scratch of a pin' (one wonders how deep the degree of anaesthesia was) and afterwards felt 'like a man newly out of a spree!'[50] This is all the more remarkable when it is remembered that the first operation carried out in public under general anaesthesia was in October 1846 in Boston, Massachusetts.[51]

CHAPTER EIGHT

General Services in the First Half of the 20th Century

FOR MANY DECADES in the 19th century virtually all medical care in the county was carried out by the general practitioners although many people, for various reasons, still sought help from the local bone-setter, blood-letter, herbalist or frank 'quack'. These GPs as we have seen, also performed surgical operations (anaesthetising as appropriate), some-times in their surgeries, sometimes in the patient's home. Their duties and responsibilities were primarily to their own individual patients but then came a new type of doctor, the MOH, at first part-time and combining the duties of the GP and then full-time from 1891 with responsibilities to the entire community.

At the beginning of the 20th century and with the advent in the county of cottage hospitals and fever hospitals which were not mere shacks for the isolation of infectious patients, a further slight shift in responsibility was seen. One of the local GPs was appointed to care for all admissions to the Town and County hospital although patients in the Bignold hospital and later, Dunbar hospital, continued to be looked after by their own practitioners.

The rapid advance in medical knowledge meant that no one doctor could hope to continue to be all things to all of his patients all of the time. Specialisation became inevitable but it was to be some years before this changed the pattern of work of Caithness GPs. Their right to admit and look after their own patients in the cottage hospitals was maintained into the 1960s although by that time they had the benefit of advice from visiting specialists from a number of medical disciplines. Resident surgical specialisation was established in the county from 1931.

Another change occurred from increasing responsibilities of the MOH who became involved in some aspects of child care as schools medical officer. He also took on clinical duties in looking after fever, tuberculous and chest patients.

There is no doubt also that the task of a GP was greatly assisted, by the beginning of the century, by vastly improved nursing support.

Problems in the Early Century

The Boer War was nothing like the drain on manpower, including medical manpower, as were the First and Second World Wars. Nevertheless a 'locum' had to be found for Dr J.K. Tomory, in practice in Halkirk, while he spent 17 months as a medical officer in South Africa.[1] Dr R.C. MacDonald and Dr J.W. Duffus who were both practitioners at Canisbay had also served in this conflict.

But most problems in medical practice in Caithness were more mundane than warfare. Not all medical officers saw eye-to-eye with their Parochial Boards and vice-versa. For example, in 1902 the local press reported in detail on the'Doctor Question in the Parish of Clyne'.[2] The people of the district were seemingly determined to get rid of him though the precise reasons for this are not clear. The matter ended in a meeting of Clyne Parish Council, described as 'lively' (usually, in these circumstances a euphemism for rowdy and ill-tempered) and although the motion to dismiss him was defeated by five votes to four, this was greeted by a very hostile, stone-throwing crowd. But this was not the norm; Dr Wright on leaving Castletown to take up practice in Wick in 1911 was presented by his grateful patients with a microscope – an indication perhaps of the extent to which the GPs of the day had to rely on his own resources for investigation and diagnosis.[3]

Many of the problems which were highlighted in the Royal College of Physicians of Edinburgh Report in the 1850s continued into the 20th century. The struggle to provide a reasonable income and satisfactory housing to attract well-qualified doctors continued. The parish clerk of Lybster wrote in 1905 to the secretary of the Congested Districts Board in Edinburgh asking for a grant towards payment of rent for the medical officer's house (which, it was said, was the only suitable and available house in the district).[4] The letter pointed out that although the Parish Council paid the doctor £50 and the Poorhouse Committee £40 per year, the doctor's private practice could not amount to much. The council had at one time wished to increase the medical officer's salary but the Local Government Board would not sanction it. The reply from the Congested Districts Board was firmly in the negative. It has to be said, however, that the doctor in this case, Dr J.R. Kennedy was not apparently deterred by such circumstances as he was still working in the area during the Second World War.

About the same time the secretary of the Canisbay Medical Association was engaged in a similar exercise but on a different tack.[5]

He was asking for an annual grant towards the salary of the Canisbay doctor. Pointing out that the salary was made up by voluntary subscriptions together with £58 from the parish council, he stressed that 'the people are poor and find it a very heavy burden to maintain their doctor'. His argument continued; 'The Parish has a population of about 2,500, 300 of whom are resident on the island of Stroma. The doctor has to cross pretty frequently at much inconvenience and sometimes great risk.' His pleas fell on deaf ears; his application was rejected.

Various sources attest to the continuing problems of medical care in the Highlands and Islands of Scotland. The Royal Commission on the Poor Law in 1904 singled out these areas as worthy of special consideration recognising that 'Medical attention in many parishes is deplorably insufficient and many of the parishes cannot maintain a doctor.' It also became apparent that the medical provisions guaranteed by the National Health Insurance Act of 1911 were impossible to deliver in outlying islands and distant glens.[6] For this reason a Committee to enquire into the Highlands and Islands medical services was set up in 1912 under the chairmanship of Sir John Dewar which resulted in the Highlands and Islands (Medical Service) Grant Act 1913 and subsequently the Highlands and Islands Medical Service.

The Highlands and Islands Medical Service

Although Caithness was not so ill provided for as some remote islands and glens it undoubtedly benefited from the service and provided some interesting evidence to the Committee which sat on 23 August 1912 in the Town Chambers, Thurso.[7] Nine doctors, a pharmacist and a post-master gave evidence, some comments being spontaneous and others obviously answers to direct questions. Dr Dick, the MOH, outlined the medical cover in the county; there were six doctors in Wick, three in Thurso, two in Latheron and one each in Canisbay, Castletown and Halkirk. Most had motor-cars (one admitting to two cars and a chauffeur) and two had motor-cycles which had to be substituted by a horse or pony and trap in winter. He explained the club system on which most of the medical care was based; families paid from 4/- upwards per annum on a sliding scale according to rent but were entitled to only a certain number of visits per year. Large farmers, he thought, took advantage of these schemes. Rural areas were not able to pay adequate fees to the doctor. He also pointed out that there was no opportunity for country doctors to attend postgraduate classes. [how this complaint echoed for decades to come!] Other comments he made were: a large proportion of midwifery cases attended by unqualified midwives and in only three parishes by trained nurses; the operations performed by GPs were not usually performed by GPs in industrial areas; uncertificated deaths were still running at 10 per cent in Caithness, mostly children a few days old or people over ninety; on the whole teeth were very bad with only two dentists in Wick; and finally he averred that tinker children were often much cleaner than others though crofters' children objected to sitting beside them.

A selection from the other evidence is given below;

> *Dr John MacLennan,* Thurso. Car mileage in the previous year, 15,832; 15 per cent of cases of illness among poor who are not paupers are not medically attended on account of inability to pay; he would prefer payment by visit; he encountered a considerable amount of bone and gland tuberculosis [reflecting infection with the bovine type of tubercle bacillus] which he treated with tuberculin with 'not particularly good results'.

> *Dr J.R. Kennedy,* Dunbeath. He claimed that GPs such as himself should receive £300 per annum net, along with a house and travelling expenses; he sent serious cases to Edinburgh and Aberdeen; GPs should have a holiday once a year with help in getting a locum who cost a guinea a day.

> *Dr J. G. MacGregor,* Castletown. No nurses were available; he undertook simple dentistry charging for a tooth extraction 2/6d with a local anaesthetic and 1/6d without.

> *Dr D. Durran,* Thurso. Described himself as Medical Superintendent of Dunbar hospital and the hospital as 'only an almshouse'; proposals to make it a general hospital had never been pursued.

> *Dr Alexander Asher,* Thurso. Also complained that Dunbar hospital did not fulfil the conditions for which it was intended and that it was managed by a self-elected Trust; he attended railway surfacemen for 6/- per annum which was deducted from their wages.

> *Mr William Gunn,* postmaster, Kinbrace. Stressed the difficulties in sending for a doctor; appeared to digress from strictly medical matters by informing the Committee that they had two churches – the Free and United Free – and that in his opinion they could do with one less!

> *Mr D.D. Cairnie,* pharmacist, Thurso. Said there was no difficulty in getting medicines dispatched and that there was no call for doctors to dispense; people doctored themselves too much with patent medicines which were expensive.

The Dewar Committee produced a wide range of well-considered and enlightened recommendations covering social conditions, communications, quality of nursing, medical remuneration and hours of work. As regards doctors' pay a firm recommendation of a minimum income of £300 per annum with travelling allowance was made. The result was the Highlands and Islands Medical Fund Act, 1913, which enabled the Highlands and Islands Medical Service (HIMS) to come into being. Its full impact was delayed by the onset of war and a boost was required by the Additional Grant Act, 1929, but there is no doubt of the great importance of the HIMS to the area. A Highland practitioner writing in 1938 quoted a description of the service as 'a unique and almost complete medical service for each specified area, a tribute alike to its organisers and to those engaged in carrying it out.' He went on to record his opinion that 'since the institution of the HIMS and the National Health Insurance, the health of the people has received attention out of all proportion to anything formerly experienced'.[8] Is it surprising that another medical writer entitled an article 'The Highlands and Islands Medical Service. A Dry Run for the NHS?'?[9]

In Caithness a notice appeared on 1 January 1916 from the HIMS Board which showed the practitioners in the scheme by parish:[10]

Bower	Dr McGregor	Castletown
	Dr McLennan	Thurso
	Dr Asher	Thurso
	Dr Leask	Wick.
Canisby	Dr Sclater	Canisby
	Dr Leask	Wick
Dunnett	Dr McGregor	Castletown
	Dr Asher	Thurso
	Dr Sclater	Canisby
Halkirk	Dr Geddie	Halkirk
	Dr Durran	Thurso
	Dr Asher	Thurso
	Dr McLennan	Thurso
	Dr Leask	Wick
Olrig	Dr Asher	Thurso
	Dr McGregor	Canisby
	Dr McLennan	Thurso
Reay	Dr Asher	Thurso
	Dr McLennan	Thurso
	Dr Durran	Thurso
	Dr Geddie	Halkirk
Thurso	Dr Asher	Thurso
	Dr McLennan	Thurso
	Dr Geddie	Halkirk
Watten	Dr Leask	Wick

	Dr Asher	Thurso
	Dr McLennan	Thurso
Wick	Dr Leask	Wick

This notice is peculiar in that some practitioners (for example, Dr Leask) appear as serving several parishes and Dr Leask is apparently the only one covering Wick; also the parish of Latheron is not mentioned. Temporary war-time arrangements may have had something to do with this.

The Inter-War Years

In 1919 the Local Government Board became the Scottish Board of Health, which in 1928 became the Department of Health for Scotland but these administrative changes had less to do with improvements in health than the public health measures taken and the provisions of the HIMS. There is no doubt about the improvements especially as regards the feared infectious diseases. The differences between mortalities in Scotland from the beginning of the century and the 1930s are striking (Table 7).

Impressions of these times are given by Dr Janet Cockcroft (née Mowat) who spent her childhood years in Lybster. Emergency operations were still the responsibility of general practitioners and she recounts how in the 1920s little Stanley Doull had his appendix successfully removed on the kitchen table with his mother who was a trained nurse assisting. Her own decision to study medicine was already influenced by the problems she saw around her, particularly those of

Table 7. Annual mortality per 100,000 alive from certain infectious diseases.

	Years 1901–10	Years 1931–39
Tuberculosis	209	77
Respiratory diseases	277	172
Typhus Group	10	0.6
Scarlet Fever	9	4
Whooping cough	44	11
Diphtheria and croup	17	9
Measles	34	9
Smallpox	1	—

Quoted from T.C. Smout (1986), *A Century of the Scottish People 1830–1950.*

women in childbirth and of children. The cost of medical attention also disturbed her and she later wrote: 'The thought went through my mind that the State ought to be providing for the women and children of the country, indeed for all the people who lived in the United Kingdom'.[11] But there were still two decades before the NHS.

John Banks was well known and respected in Caithness and his acquaintance with medical matters and doctors was enhanced by his chairmanship of the Canisbay Medical Association and later, of the Caithness Health Executive Council. He has recorded several stories, not all reflecting sweetness and accord with the local doctors. One bone of contention which eventually reached the Department of Health concerned charges for the use of the boat to take the doctor to and from Stroma. A delegation, including Banks, from the Association confronted the doctor and did not mince words. Banks writes; 'We had to state very firmly that we were of the opinion that he had been fraudulently retaining moneys being paid to him for the use of boats in which he had no material interest.'[12] This happily resulted in an agreement for certain payments to the boatmen and no more trouble was experienced. After the first World War there came to a head an even more unpleasant matter concerning the Canisbay doctor of the time. He had over a period of years lost the confidence of many of his patients. This was aired with some passion in the local press and the Association finally dismissed him as medical practitioner for the parish, giving him three months notice and asking him to vacate his house (which was provided by the Association). The doctor refused to accept his dismissal and took legal advice which eventually resulted in a public enquiry set up by the Department of Health for Scotland, chaired by senior counsel. This vindicated the Association and the department advised the doctor to leave the practice and retire which he did.

Other interesting facets of medicine in Canisbay are revealed by John Banks. It was the pattern, he writes, for many patients to consult doctors privately in Wick – presumably during the time of their unhappy relationship with their own GP. He describes the importance of tuberculosis in peoples lives, including members of his own family who were treated in a sanatorium in Invergordon. He also tells of how people clutched at straws in their search for effective treatment. His own sister was charged £100 (a very considerable sum in those days) for a course of 'serum' from a Swiss doctor at a London Hospital. Another proprietary 'cure', popular and expensive at the time, consisted of water with a little garlic added.[13]

Plate 24. Health Clinic, Wick; housed in the old harbour jail (From 'Times Gone Bye', North of Scotland Newspapers Ltd).

At this time there was an increasing awareness amongst the public of what could and should be done to improve health. The Townswomen's Guild of Wick took up cudgels on behalf of children's health by demanding that a child welfare clinic be set up. The health of children had received special attention in the Education (Scotland) Act of 1908 which empowered the formation of a school health service. In 1910 the Caithness branch of the Educational Institute for Scotland (EIS) was highlighting the financial implications of the medical inspection of schoolchildren; a sum of £555 was deemed necessary, this being broken down into £300 for the MO's salary, £50 for travelling expenses, £35 for incidentals and £170 for apparatus.[14] The problem was resolved by combining the post of MO for schools with that of the county MOH and in 1911 Dr Dick was appointed with a salary of £200 per annum. For a time, he had also been MOH for Sutherland as well as Caithness but on his schools' appointment he demitted the Sutherland post.* Later, when an assistant to the MOH was appointed responsibilities of schools MO was devolved on her. At the beginning of the Second World War

---

*Sutherland did not lose its Caithness public health connection. It appointed as its MOH, Dr Bremner, a native of Freswick and an Edinburgh graduate who had been Dux of Pultneytown Academy.

the first incumbent was Dr Janet Bruce, followed by Dr Janet Mowat. The clinic pressed for by the Townswomen's Guild was housed in the unprepossessing building which was formerly the harbour jail built by the Pultneytown Commissioners for the British Fishermen's Society in the middle of the 19th century (Plate 24).[15] It is likely this was staffed by district nurses with supervision by one of the local practitioners. Later the Wick and Pultneytown District Nursing Association make a gift of a building in Sinclair Terrace which was known as the Bruce Memorial child welfare clinic.

The kind of work undertaken by the schools medical service and the information it produced is exemplified in the accompanying table (Table 8). The material is taken from an appendix to the MOH Report for 1936, relating to schools medical inspections in Caithness. Perhaps the most startling and disturbing fact from this is the mere 11 per cent of children who had sound teeth. It is also difficult to know what was labelled 'functional' heart disease in children.

The health statistics prepared by the MOH continued to show the changes in incidence and mortality of diseases. For example, in 1936, Thurso with a population of 3,088 had a total of 46 deaths of which nearly a half were due to heart disease and stroke. There was only one death from pulmonary tuberculosis and only five from other infectious diseases, all pneumonias. Of the twelve infectious diseases notified, six were of non-pulmonary tuberculosis, two each of diphtheria and scarlet fever and one each of erysipelas and puerperal pyrexia.[16] Wick with a population of 7,550 produced similar figures. Forty four notifications of infectious diseases included 21 of scarlet fever and 9 of tuberculosis.[17]

The slow decline in the incidence of smallpox has been well recorded and eradication on a world basis was achieved in the 1970s. Apathy with regard to the vaccination of children was still a problem and in Wick in 1925 the Parish Council was concerned that 98 children remained unprotected and sent notices to the parents or guardians and the parish vaccinator. Dr Leask later replied that all but three had been vaccinated but that the parents of the three, despite repeated warnings,had refused to allow their children to be so treated. The Council responded by instructing the Sanitary Inspector to write to each parent giving notice that if the children were not vaccinated within four weeks that proceedings would be taken against them in terms of the Vaccination Act. The outcome of this is not recorded. In passing, the salary of the parish medical officer was £40 per annum for the Poor Law obligations, £10 for vaccination and £10 for Lunacy Act obligations.[18]

Table 8. Medical Inspection of Schoolchildren in Caithness, 1936.

Cleanliness of Head and Body.
    Head dirty – 9.8%   Nits or vermin – 3.2%
    Body dirty – 10.4%   Nits or vermin – 0.4%

Condition of Skin

	Boys	Girls
Impetigo	0.3%	0.16%
Scabies	—	0.33%
Others	1.1%	0.84%

Nutrition	Below average	10.3%
Teeth	Sound	11.2%
Mental Capacity	Very backward	3.3%

Heart and Circulation
    Organic disease   0.58% (Number – 7)
    Functional disease 3.1% (Number – 36)

Tuberculosis
    Suspected pulmonary 9   (0.75%)
    Glands   5
    Bone and joint 3

Any account of infectious diseases in the first half of this century is incomplete without mention of the disastrous pandemic of influenza which swept the world in 1918–1919. It is estimated that five hundred million people were affected world wide and that of these fifteen million died.[19] Caithness, of course, did not escape and we know something of the local problems from the observations of Dr Leask of Wick whose MD thesis was on this subject.[20] He estimated that he was medically responsible at that time for eight thousand people and that between the 1 July 1918 and 31 December 1919 he treated 'about two thousand' cases of influenza of which the surprisingly low number of 14 died. This equates to a crude death rate of 1.75 per thousand population whereas the crude death rate for the whole of Scotland was 4.3 per thousand. Caithness as a whole suffered one hundred deaths from the epidemic giving a death rate of 4.1 per thousand.

What is noteworthy is that the 14 deaths encountered by Dr Leask were mostly in young adults; there were no old people (the oldest was 38) and only one child of 12. The symptoms he encountered were what one would expect in influenza although he records that many had severe epistaxis (nose bleeds) and 'a great fear of the illness itself'.

The belief at that time was that the illness was due to a bacterium (Bacillus influenzae). We know now of course that it is due to a virus and that our modern antibiotics combat secondary infection only. Dr Leask's treatment was palliative although he makes strong claims in his thesis for a particular combination of medicaments known as Pil.phenacetin co. (compound phenacetin pill) which contained the following:

Phenacetin	grains 3
Quinine sulphate	grains 2
Pulv. Ipeca. co.*	grains 1/2
Ext. Aconit.	grains 1/8

*This contained ipecacuanha and opium.

When influenzal pnuemonia threatened or occurred he used a mixture (which he admitted was difficult to take especially by children) of iodide and creosote. Whatever the reasons, his patients did remarkably well in this devastating epidemic.

The Nursing Services

By the 20th century nursing had become a well organised and trained profession. Nurses in the early 19th century were not well regarded and Charles Dicken's infamous Sarah Gamp typified a substantial number of nurses at that time. Formal training for nurses was started at the Nightingale Training School at St Thomas's Hospital, London in 1860, and Edinburgh Royal Infirmary was training nurses, shortly after this. Teaching hospitals around the country soon started their own training programmes and other hospitals followed. The reference to a nurse in Wick during the 1849 cholera epidemic would therefore imply she was not formally trained but by the time the Wick Combination Fever Hospital was established in the 1890s, nurse training was available outwith the county. There is little doubt that the senior nurses working in the hospitals would have had such training. Also by then nursing had become a respected profession, one to which many Caithness young women were attracted. Some returned to work in their home county; others never did and contributed to the great export of nursing talent over the decades, similar to an equally important medical export.

Even at the beginning of this century some country areas relied on the 'howdy', an untrained midwife or sick-nurse or a woman who laid out the dead. Of nurses with some training, Caithness would almost certainly have had representatives from the following categories.

1. Maternity nurses. A woman, generally a widow who had attended a course of lectures and a certain number of confinements under supervision.

2. Cottage nurses. (a) Trained in maternity and general medical and surgical nursing for six to twelve months; (b) As above, but taking the certificate of the Central Midwives Board at one of the recognised maternity hospitals. This corresponded to the qualifications of the 'Govan Homes for Cottage Nurses' (these were usually referred to as 'Govan nurses').

3. Fully trained nurses. This implied three years training in a recognised hospital of not less than 100 beds. The nurses supplied to the Highlands and Islands by the Queen Victoria Jubilee Institute (see below) were of this category.[21]

Many of the parishes had invoked a spirit of self-help by starting nursing associations along the same lines as the medical associations. Local lairds often installed a nurse at their own expense although there is no record of this happening in Caithness. An impetus was given at the time of Queen Victoria's Golden Jubilee in 1887. The women of Britain collected £70,000 to celebrate this event. The Queen made it known that she wished this money to be used for the promotion of home nursing for the sick and in 1889 the Queen Victoria Jubilee Institute for Nursing was incorporated. £10,000 of the above sum was allocated to Scotland and in its first year the Edinburgh centre had trained eight district nurses increasing numbers year by year until in 1909 it trained 39. The Queen also established what became an important part of the ethos of district nursing – that the nurse be a 'sanitary missionary', promoting basic rules of hygiene and health and knowing what charities to approach when in need of food, clothing and bedding.[22]

Wick and Pultneytown appointed a nurse from the Institute in 1893 and a local District Nursing Association was formed. This body was very much concerned with raising funds to pay the nurses salary. In the same year Dr McLean of Thurso, at a meeting of the Public Health Committee of the Caithness County Council, was emphasising the importance of the MOH's recommendation that there should be a trained nurse for the county. He reported: 'People in Caithness do not know what proper nursing is and think any old woman will do'.[23] Other places followed suit, for example Thurso in 1900 and Reay in 1910. In 1933 it was recommended that a trained nurse be placed on Stroma.[24]

Plate 25. Wick VADs, 1925–27. From the Johnston Collection (Reproduced by permission of the, Wick Society).

In 1901 Wick and Pultneytown District Nursing Association employed two nurses (Nurse Donald and Nurse Noble) who that year had attended to 201 new cases and had made 6,347 visits. Money raised by the Association went not only towards salaries but to nursing appliances, garments for the poor and perhaps most importantly nourishment for the sick in the form of beef-tea, milk and eggs.[25] Part of other expenses in 1914 for Latheron Association (where the nurse had made 1458 visits in the year) was for a new bicycle. Before the advent of the NHS and during the time of the HIMS it was the aim to have two district nurses in every parish engaged and paid by local nursing associations. In the 1950s Caithness was recorded as having fifteen district nurses.[26]

An example of the exodus of young women from Caithness who left to train as nurses and to work elsewhere is Nurse Jessie Sutherland, daughter of Charles Sutherland of Mid Clyth. She became a ward sister at the Royal Free Hospital, London, and in 1915 volunteered for service with the British Red Cross hospital in Serbia.[27] Other nurses in Caithness were similarly motivated. Miss McGillivray who has been mentioned as first matron of the Town and County hospital volunteered in 1914 for service with the Scottish Womens hospital, also in Serbia where her devoted nursing of typhoid fever patients almost cost her her own life and left her with a permanent disability. She served the Town and County hospital for 27 years retiring in 1942, having had a remarkable escape in the air crash in 1941. She died in the Bignold hospital while on a holiday visit to Wick in 1951.[28] Other women, unable to undertake the lengthy, formal training in nursing, found satisfaction in an auxiliary role and became members of Voluntary Aid Detachments (VADs) That Caithness had no lack of such volunteers who gave excellent services in emergencies and routine duties is seen from the photograph of the Wick detachment of 1925–27 (Plate 25). As the century progressed the district nurses' bicycles were replaced by motor cars (Austin Sevens being particularly popular). She often lived in a house specially built or provided for her by the associations in the same way that medical practitioners' houses were provided. With the advent of the NHS district nursing services came under the control of the Local Authority.

Some Doctors of the Early Century

Up to the beginning of the 20th century women did not play a prominent role in medicine. Only one Caithness woman, Dr Irene Coghill, appears to have graduated in medicine in the 19th century but at the turn of the century and up to the Second World War the situation changed. During this period a number of women doctors with addresses in Caithness appeared in the Medical Directory. Some were born in Caithness but went on to work elsewhere; some changed their names through marriage and are difficult to trace and others are incomers. They are in roughly chronological order as follows:

    Dr Elizabeth McHardy, Latheron (MBChB Aber. 1909)
    Dr Helen Lillie, Wick (MBChB Aber. 1914)
    Dr Janet Rugg, Wick (MBChB Edin. 1919. H.S. Bolton Infirmary)
    Dr Helen Sutherland, Wick (MBChB Glas. 1920. Daughter of Revd Mr Sutherland, Bruan)
    Dr Jessie Dower, Halkirk (MBChB Edin. 1922. Moved to Invergordon.)
    Dr Margaret Bruce, Wick. (MBChBEdin. 1924)
    Dr Anne McLennan, Thurso (MBChB Aber. 1925)
    Dr Christina Ross, Wick. (MBChB 1924)
    Dr Bertha Flintoff, Thurso. (MBChB Durham 1924)
    Dr Catherine Sutherland, Thurso (MBChB Edin. 1939)
    Dr Doris MacIntosh, Wick, (MBChB Vict. 1920 Late Ass. School MO Stockport.)
    Dr Janet Mowat, Lybster, (MBChB Glas. 1938)
    Dr Reena McLennan, Thurso, (MBChB Glas. 1920. Daughter of Revd Mr McLennan, Reay)

Of these doctors more is known of two of them:

Dr Helen Lillie (Garrett). Although born in Eday, Orkney, in 1890, Helen Lillie spent her childhood at the Manse, Watten, where her father was minister, the family having Caithness connections going back to 1884. She qualified MBChB at Aberdeen in 1914, (Plate 26) thereafter gaining surgical experience in Sheffield. In 1915 she did a locum in general practice in Latheron where this young woman doctor so impressed that she was asked to stay but she was 'no so minded'.[29] Other more adventurous tasks were in her sights; she was one of that indomitable band of women who served with the Scottish Womens' Hospitals (SWH) in the 1914-18 War. In Ostrovo in Serbia she served under Dr Bennet who having watched her operate, later wrote 'I felt I had never seen a woman do an operation so deftly and so quickly.'[30]

Plate 26. Dr Helen Lillie (Reproduced by courtesy of Mr W. Garrett).

Despite the pressure of her surgical work she found time to gather material for an MD thesis entitled 'Malaria with special reference to cases treated in Macedonia'. Early in 1918 she arrived at the SWH at Royamount in France where she again treated battle casualties straight from the front. After the war she prepared herself for work overseas by taking the Diploma in Tropical Medicine and in 1920 went to the Dufferin Hospital, Calcutta, and then to the Church of Scotland Mission Hospital in Sialkot in the Punjab. There she met and married the Revd John Garrett. Returning to Scotland after the Second World War and after her husband's death she failed to find medical work and became a librarian at Glasgow University Library. Her active life ended in 1963 when she had a serious car accident in Poland and she died aged 86 in 1977. Many from Caithness will remember her sister Mary who became the 'Lady of the Manse' looking after the Revd Mr Lillie until he died in 1941. She herself died in 1995 at the age of 102.[31]

Dr Janet Mowat (Cockcroft). A daughter of Major W.G. Mowat MC JP, draper of Lybster, she qualified MBChB at Glasgow in 1938. After assistanships in general practice she returned to Lybster in 1943 and was appointed assistant MOH with responsibility for schools. As has been mentioned she was particularly interested in the problems of women and children and the rest of her professional life reflected this. Work with family planning and antenatal and baby clinics and later with the National Council for Women (of which she became president), and the United Nations States of Women Commission (of which she became chairman) absorbed her manifest energies. All this devoted work resulted in the award of an OBE in 1975.[32] Her brother Bill is well-known in Caithness and is a former Provost of Wick.

Her younger sister Mary also graduated in medicine but while working in general practice in Ripley with her husband Dr Ross Thomson, died at the early age of 46 but the Mowat family association with medicine did not end there. Two of Janet Mowat's uncles were distinguished surgeons. Allan Mowat became senior surgeon and chief Medical Officer, Uganda, and George T. Mowat was a well-known surgeon in Glasgow, who was still working as a locum consultant when he died at the age of 71. Graduating in 1914 he had a distinguished career as a medical officer in the First World War in Salonika and Italy being awarded the Italian Bronze Medal for Military Valour.

Dr J.R. Kennedy: graduated MBCM from Aberdeen University in 1893 and came to Caithness in 1900. He served the people of the Dunbeath area until his retirement in 1947. As we have seen he gave evidence to the Dewar Committee in 1912 and it was he who led the rescue party in 1942 (when he was in his seventies) to the air crash which killed the Duke of Kent and other RAF men. When he was warned of the possibility of bombs on board the aircraft (the nature of the flight mission was not known) he is reported to have said, 'To heck with bombs, there may be human beings yet alive'.[33] Dr Kennedy was a courageous man but was known to be robust of speech and almost certainly did not use the word 'heck'. For this exploit he was made a Member of the Royal Victorian Order.

Dr A. Dingwall Kennedy. A native of Argyllshire he came to Wick in 1910 having graduated MBChB at Glasgow in 1903. He served the community in panel and private practice and for a time as medical superintendent of the Town and County hospital, until his death in 1933. Not only did he volunteer as a student for medical service in the South African War, he served overseas in the medical branch of the Royal Flying Corps in the 1914-18 War.[34]

Dr James Leask graduated MBChB in Aberdeen 1907 and took his MD in 1920. He practised in Wick from 1910 when he acted as a locum for Dr Eliot who, as we have see, was one of the earliest MO's to the Bignold Hospital. He took over the practice on Dr Eliot's death shortly after and worked from surgeries in Sinclair Terrace, then Stafford Place and finally at number 8 High Street.[35] He was joined in practice in 1946 and then succeeded , when he died in 1948, by his son Dr James C. Leask. Leask, senior, in addition to being a popular and caring GP took his wider responsibilities to the community seriously. For example, he frequently lectured to lay audiences on diverse subjects from 'Louis Pasteur' (to the Mercantile Debating Society – proceeds to the Bignold hospital) to 'Personal Hygiene' (to Watten Young Men's Mutual Improvement Association).[36]

A photograph taken in 1910 or 1911 (Plate 27) shows Dr Leask senior in his car with his chauffeur and a friend in front of Aukengill School. The number plate is interesting as it appears to indicate that this was the second motor car to be licensed in Caithness.

Dr William Barnetson. Although born in Caithness he spent most of the professional life as a medical officer in the Colonial Medical Service in Uganda. Before this he had graduated MBChB at Aberdeen in 1934 and had taken his DTM&H at Liverpool.[37] His widow became a well-known figure in the Red Cross and other circles in Caithness.

Glass, in his account of Caithness and the Second World War lists those service men and women with Caithness connections who died on

Plate 27. Dr James Leask Sen., with chauffeur and friend in his car (circa 1910)
(Reproduced by courtesy of Dr James Leask).

service and those who were decorated for gallantry. Several of these were doctors:

1. The Medalists

Dr Malcolm Manson. The fourth son of Mr Alex. Manson, of Gills, Canisbay, he had served in the RAMC in the First World War when he won a Military Cross. His gallantry continued in the Second World War when as a medical officer in Wood Green, London, he won a George Medal for his work during air raids in 1941.

Surgeon Lieutenant F.R. Badenoch, RNVR, grandson of Mr and Mrs Francis Reid, North Keiss, was awarded an MBE.

Lt. Colonel A. Tait, RAMC. Grandson of Mrs Morrison, Thurso; mentioned in dispatches.

2. The Roll of Honour

Surgeon Lieutenant Commander RM Bremner, GM. Killed in an air raid in 1942.

Flight Lieutenant W.M. Cross, RAF Medical Branch. Died on active service in 1941. Late of Annadale.

Captain James Manson, RAMC. Killed in France in 1940. Grandson of Mr and Mrs Manson, Dempster Street, Wick.

J.K. Sutherland MRCP, MRCOG. Died 1940. Youngest son of James Sutherland.

Lieutenant J.P. Thyne, RAMC. Posted missing 1940. His wife (née McKenzie) belonged to Mid Clyth.

CHAPTER NINE

The NHS Hospitals

WITH THE END OF THE SECOND WORLD WAR, the medical services in the United Kingdom faced many and radical changes. Six years of costly, unrelenting war effort resulted in medical facilities needing renovation. Thousands of medical and nursing personel returned to civilian life from the armed forces looking for satisfying posts in general practice and hospitals. Political change ensured that medical administration would be fundamentally altered. Thought was given to these coming changes even during the conflict but peace brought impetus to the process and the Scottish Hospitals Survey of 1946 reviewed the problems and suggested ways forward.

That part of the report dealing with the Northern Region gave some interesting background information on population and crude health statistics. (Table 9). It summarised the hospital and hospital staffing position at that time. The region had one main general hospital (Royal Northern Infirmary, 205 beds) and one country general hospital (Raigmore, an EMS [Emergency Medical Service] hospital, of 468 beds.) Caithness had two cottage hospitals (Bignold – 28 beds, and Dunbar – 36 beds) one maternity hospital (Henderson nursing home – 8 beds), one infectious diseases hospital (Town and County hospital – 33

Table 9. *Population Distribution and Health Statistics,*
Northern Region 1945.

District	Population	Births	Deaths Pulmonary TB	Deaths Non-pulmonary TB	Deaths Maternal	Deaths Malignant Disease
Caithness County	25, 742	458	10	3	1	38
Ross & Cromarty	62,846	940	47	8	5	109
Sutherland	15,293	240	5	2	2	37
Inverness County	58,026	865	19	11	3	88
Inverness	23,316	388	10	1	2	54
TOTALS	185,223	2,891	91	25	13	320

From *Scottish Hospitals Survey*, Department of Health for Scotland 1946. Edinburgh HMSO.

beds) and one Poor Law institution (Town and County Home, Latheron).

The report's recommendations as regards the three voluntary hospitals in Caithness were that in the short-term the Bignold hospital should resume its pre-war functions, take over from the RAF, and in the long-term be replaced by a new cottage hospital associated with and on the site of the Henderson nursing home. This was to have 20 surgical beds, 6 medical beds, a children's ward of 6 beds and an infectious diseases block of 10 beds. The old Bignold would then be used for chronic sick and advanced cases of pulmonary tuberculosis. Dunbar hospital was to continue as it was with an increase in maternity beds and better outpatient accommodation. A reduction in surgical work was envisaged there when the new cottage hospital in Wick was built. The Henderson home which, it was stated, took chiefly private cases and excluded unmarried mothers (a statement not seen elsewhere) was over-taxed in its accommodation. The recommendation was that it should be replaced as soon as possible by a new maternity unit of 12 beds on the same site.

The Town and County hospital, one of the two local authority hospitals in the county, was to continue to provide 18 beds for infectious disease and 10 for pulmonary tuberculosis (5 beds were allocated for staff accommodation.) In the long term it was to be incorporated in the plans for the Bignold hospital. The Town and County Home at Latheron, an old Poor law Institution, was said to accommodate 50 'inmates' with eight beds for chronic sick and three maternity beds. The report stated, 'The building is dark and damp and quite unsuitable for chronic sick or for any other type of case; it has been condemned.'[1] Not surprisingly the recommendation was the removal of chronic sick as soon as possible.

The survey also highlighted the inadequacies of hospital staffing and specialist service provision. There was a physician at the EMS hospital at Raigmore but the first appointment of a consulting physician under the HIMS was in 1938 at the Royal Northern Infirmary [RNI], Inverness, where he had clinical charge of 48 beds and was assisted by three GP physicians. He also conducted outpatient clinics at Fort William, Wick or Thurso (monthly), Golspie (bi-monthly) and Stornoway (three-monthly). That the work was regarded as 'beyond one man's capacity' and that there was urgent need for assistance is not surprising. Two general surgeons were in private practice in Inverness who also had charge of 82 beds at RNI. There were HIMS surgeons at Fort William, Stornoway, Golspie and Wick. The survey emphasised the unsatisfactory circumstances of these four surgeons. The main points were that they worked in permanent and almost complete professional isolation and that locums were difficult to obtain.

A summary of the position of other specialities in the region is as follows; psychological medicine – provision almost entirely lacking; dermatology – none; orthopaedic surgery – one consultant appointed in 1943 to Raigmore and RNI; ophthalmology – two surgeons at RNI; ENT – one surgeon at RNI; paediatrics – none; radiology – one consultant at RNI; obstetrics – up to 1940 all obstetrics done by GPs with help from general surgeons – 1940, consultant at RNI; anaesthetics – all anaesthetics in region administered by GPs or hospital residents; pathology services – 'small outpost laboratories established in the Lewis hospital, Stornoway and in the proposed new hospitals in Fort William and Wick would be of great value.'

The new administrative structure of the NHS in the north of Scotland had to follow in the wake of this survey and its recommendations. Some recommendations were not acted upon; some were accepted with modifications, and others took a long time to be implemented but there is no doubt that they had a generally beneficial effect on the hospital services in Caithness.

The New Administrative Structures

The National Health Services (Scotland) Act 1947 was the instrument whereby the NHS was established in Scotland. In the north of Scotland the Northern Regional Hospital Board devolved day-to-day running of hospitals in Caithness to the Board of Management for Caithness hospitals. (referred to hereafter as 'the Caithness Board' or simply 'the Board'). This Board had its inaugural meeting on 18 June 1948 at Mackay's Hotel, Wick to arrange a smooth take-over on the appointed day, 5 July. The original Board was:

Ex-Provost J. Harper – Chairman
Sherrif G. Cormack Cohen – Vice Chairman
Councillor Miss J. Cormack
Mr J.S. Banks
Dr W.I. A. Fell
Mr W.F. Dunnett
Ex-Provost Peter Sutherland
Dr R.F. MacDonald MOH[2]

The Board appointed Mr A.B. Campbell, solicitor, Wick as its secretary. Later this post was held for many years by Mr John Graham, solicitor, Wick.

The Board and its successors controlled the four Caithness hospitals with the help of house committees for each. At that time each hospital retained its medical superintendent, Dr Dick at the Bignold, Mr Roxburgh at the Dunbar and Dr Ramsay at the Henderson hospitals. The MOH acted as district hospitals officer and had clinical duties for infectious diseases and tuberculosis at the Town and County hospital. The consultant surgeon had charge of surgical services at the Bignold and Dunbar but medical, obstetrical and anaesthetic cases were the responsibility of general practitioners.

From this time it became increasingly difficult to regard the four Caithness hospitals as totally separate entities. With the opening of the Central hospital in 1966 as the first phase of the future general hospital and as a specialist medical hospital, they were increasingly recognised as surgical, medical and obstetric units of a yet to be general hospital, albeit with continuing GP services and separate sites.

Financial Matters

The new Caithness Board had to grapple with all the hospitals' running costs on a tight budget. In the year 1954–55 the total costs were £42,605, the Bignold and Dunbar absorbing the bulk of these at about £13,000 each, the Town and County almost £11,000 and the Henderson just over £5,000. Salaries and wages accounted for £26,520 of the total (nursing salaries being the heaviest item at £15,996) and supplies and services absorbing the remainder.[3] Only a few years before however in 1949, the sum available to the Board was only £32,546 which, of course, was to cover all expenditure except building.[4]

Although the NHS was introduced on the basis of no charge to patients, the system of pay-beds was retained. Early in 1949 the Henderson charged £7 per week for a single room and £5 for a double; the Dunbar with 2 single rooms charged £3 3s per week while the Bignold and Town and County made no charge for private rooms.[5] The Board learned however that it now had financial masters in Inverness, the NRHB intimating that it thought the Henderson charges were excessive and instructing that they be reduced to £3 3s and £2 2s respectively.[6] Later, the Bignold made a charge of £1 10s for such accommodation.

By the 1940s even small voluntary hospitals had accumulated substantial Endowment Funds and the Board became the Trustees for the Caithness hospitals. Much anxiety was expressed about what would happen to these funds. Their fate in Scotland was determined by the Endowments Commission which was empowered to direct that a proportion of these be transferred to regional hospital boards and to allocate some to a central fund for medical research. In 1951 the Caithness Board minuted that it was the intention of the Commission to take 40 per cent of funds for research purposes. This, it was said, would mean the loss of £32,000 and a loss in annual income of over £900.[7] This was a few months after a request from the Department of Health for £5,240 from endowments had been paid.[8] In the main, endowment funds were used for minor items not covered from central resources although it was at one time suggested that the cost of a new hospital be met partly from these. Later, in 1965 the Trustees offered ground at the Henderson to build a medical centre for GP's but this was not taken up at the time.[9]

The Work of the Hospitals and their Future

The pattern of work in the first year of the NHS was very similar to that before the war. For example, the Bignold dealt with 458 in-patients and 2,068 out-patients; 195 minor operations and 192 other operations were carried out and 1,165 X-ray plates taken.[10] A sample of monthly admissions (Table 10) albeit without average number of days in hospital and no indication of bed turnover suggests the accommodation was not under pressure.[11] This is reflected in the views of a deputation from the Wick branch of the Royal British Legion to the Board, pointing out that facilities, particularly at the Bignold, were not being used to the full and that too many patients were being sent to Inverness. In reply it was said that these decisions rested with the medical attendants and that no one was sent unnecessarily.[12] Part of the problem may have been the

Table 10. Admission Statistics Caithness Hospitals, January 1950.

	Admissions	Deaths	Births	No. in hospital on last day of month
Bignold hospital	34	1	–	16
Dunbar hospital	34	1	7	15
Henderson nursing home	19	–	18	5
Town & County hospital				
1. Tuberculosis	4	2	–	9
2. Infectious Diseases	1	1	–	3

perennial hospital one of inability to transfer the chronic sick to appropriate accommodation. This was certainly so at the Dunbar where it was said the normal medical and surgical work of the hospital was being held up.[13]

Only four years after the 1946 Scottish Hospitals Survey the Caithness Board was considering the options for the future. It agreed with the recommendations of a Special Sub-Committee which had clearly been influenced by the Survey and largely agreed with its conclusions.[14] Nevertheless, a decade later the concept of a new centralised hospital on the Henderson (Rosebank) site (which the Board had fully supported on the basis of economy and efficiency) was nowhere near realisation. The need, obvious in the immediate post-war years, was even more so by the 1960s, because of population changes within the county. The building of the Dounreay Experimental Reactor Establishment near Thurso caused the population of Thurso alone to rise from 4,210 in 1951 to 8,922 in 1961 and later to over 10,000. This was not a simple increase in poulation; the demographic structure was altered and to the traditional fishing, farming and crofting communities were grafted numbers of scientists and engineers and their families.

In 1960 the Board was urging the NRHB to treat the matter of hospital accommodation in the county as a matter of urgency but was told there was little hope of this for a long time. At its meeting the Board 'expressed its profound disappointment'.[15] The position was such that the county clerk, on the instruction of Caithness County Council wrote to the NRHB about hospital services in Thurso and the need for increased accommodation. In reply, the secretary of the NRHB, perhaps predictably, provided statistics; he opined that the Dunbar had been able to deal with the increased load without difficulty because it had not been used previously to its full capacity. He quoted the year 1959, the year with the highest rate of admissions, as having a bed occupancy of only 58 per cent, the lowest of any small general hospital in the Northern Region.[16] At the same time the NRHB indicated that it had taken up with the Department of Health the question of a consultant physician for Caithness. The County Council did not appear to be reassured or impressed by this and the following year the county clerk wrote again at some length and detail to the NRHB in support of the Caithness Board. He recorded the 'growing feeling of unrest' in the county and asked that 'immediate and urgent consideration' be given to the review of hospital accommodation.[17] It was to be a further five years before the first phase of the new hospital was opened.

Caithness Central Hospital (CCH)

This was the name given to the new unit, built, within the Rosebank grounds, to act as the first specialist medical unit in Caithness and to be the first phase of the general hospital on the same site. A single story building, it had 26 beds in 4 bedded and single wards and included treatment rooms, a laboratory, dispensary and facilities for relatives of patients to stay overnight if necessary.

Its formal opening on 9 August 1966 was a Royal occasion. Queen Elizabeth the Queen Mother arrived just as sunshine broke through a dense haar. Mr John Sinclair, the Lord Lieutenant of the county met her and Provost Dunnett, chairman of the Caithness Hospitals Board

Plate 28. Opening of Caithness Central Hospital. Rona Boyd presents the Queen Mother with a bouquet, with the Lord Lieutenant, Mr John Sinclair, in attendance (From the author's collection).

of Management at the time, gave a speech of welcome. The traditional bouquet of flowers was presented by ten year old Rona Boyd (Plate 28) and after unveiling a wall plaque the Queen Mother was escorted on a tour of the unit by the consultant physician and matron. What proved to be a memorable day in every way was rounded off by tea in a marquee in the grounds.[18]

From its inception the new unit admitted patients from Caithness and adjacent parts of Sutherland. These patients were suffering from acute medical emergencies or requiring specialist investigations and treatment regimes. This was possible not only from the staff expertise available but because of equipment and service facilities not before available in the county. The laboratory, small though it was, was a very important part of this. Essential biochemical, haematological and bacteriological tests could be carried out on the spot and would no longer be dependent on a postal service to Inverness. Later, and with the co-operation of the staff at Dounreay, more sophisticated diagnostic investigations such as the use of medical isotope material were possible.

The Central hospital also provided a venue for local professional meetings, most of those attending being general practitioners. Sunday mornings were the time for the presentation of clinical cases and discussions which contributed to everyone's continuing medical education. Those attending formed the Caithness Medical Society which later invited speakers from afar. On one occasion the Society was fortunate enough to have as a guest speaker Sir Derek Dunlop, Professor of Therapeutics at Edinburgh whose talk was followed by a well-attended dinner at the Portland Arms in Lybster. Continuing medical education for hospital doctors and GPs alike is now well established and organised. In Caithness it had tentative beginnings in the 1960s.

Specialist Obstetric Services

Two years after the appointment of a consultant physician, a consultant obstetrician and gynaecologist was appointed in 1966. These appointments together with the established presence of a surgeon meant that the three major specialties were now represented in the county and a scattered nucleus of a small district general hospital was in existence. The presence of an obstetrician inevitably meant a re-allocation of beds in the hospitals and the Dunbar hospital was ear-marked for the specialist obstetric and gynaecological beds, plus a few cots for premature and special care babies. That these provisions were required is borne out by the MOH's report for 1967 when he recorded that

Caithness had the third highest birth-rate for any county in Scotland (21.4 births per 1,000 of the population compared with a national average of 18.9).[19] By 1986 the benefits of the service were apparent again in the MOH's report, that because of the ante-natal and post-natal clinics it was now rarely necessary to transfer patients south for specialist treatment of mothers and young children.[20]

The implications of the new obstetrical service were, of course, that all surgical patients were dealt with at Bignold hospital and that beds were no longer available for medical patients on a cottage hospital basis at the Dunbar hospital. It was recognised that the beds available at the Bignold would be insufficient to meet the needs of surgical patients and ten beds were therefore made available at the Town and County hospital in a re-opened ward for convalescent surgical patients. In the mid-sixties the Town and County bed complement was thirteen for infectious diseases and twenty for chronic sick.

It has to be said that the changes in the hospital services did not please everyone and this was especially so of those in the north and west of the county. This is reflected in the correspondence columns of local newspapers which claimed that Thurso should have a general hospital of its own. An argument might have been put forward for this, but there was never a need for two general hospitals in the county. One correspondent asserted that Thurso had been better provided with hospitals fifty years previously when it had the Burnside hospital![21] Nor did citizens in the Wick area accept with equanimity the changes that took place. In 1978 the Henderson Memorial Home closed but the Caithness Local Health Council (voicing the views of those mostly in the eastern part of the county) called for maternity services at Wick to be 're-established at the earliest possible date'.[22]

Caithness General Hospital (CGH)

From the opening of the Central Hospital in 1966, a further two decades were to elapse before the new integrated Caithness General Hospital was formally opened in 1987. The transfer of patients from the other hospitals to the new hospital was phased. It was not until December 1986 that the last of the surgical patients and staff vacated Bignold hospital, and it was entirely appropriate that the last member of staff to leave was Sister Sarah Leith who had given unequalled service to the hospital for thirty years.[23]

The day of the official opening, 25 August 1987, was another Royal occasion with the Queen Mother delighting everyone with her presence as she had done 21 years previously . Greeted by the Lord Lieutenant, Lord Thurso and by Mr James McWilliam, Chairman of the Highland Health Board, she unveiled another plaque and then made a tour of the hospital escorted by Mr John McLean, Director of Nursing Services. It was fitting that the surgical unit had been given the name Bignold, the maternity unit Henderson and the medical unit, Rosebank. The old Central hospital, the first phase of the new hospital and now the geriatric unit, was to be known as the Queen Elizabeth wing.

The new hospital, built at a cost of £8.6 million, has 121 beds divided between the three major specialities and assessment and rehabilitation. These are supported by the appropriate departments − radiology, laboratory, physiotherapy, occupational therapy and pharmacy. To staff these and all the other essential functions of a modern hospital requires a complement of some three hundred people.

It was perhaps naïve of people to think that all would be immediately well. Such a large and complex exercise inevitably would have its teething troubles. For example the local Member of Parliament, Mr Robert McLennan, voiced his concern that so many beds were left unoccupied, a situation ascribed to lack of funding by the Health Board.[24] Because of initial staffing difficulties, the ante-natal clinic at the Dunbar hospital had to be temporarily stopped with patients required to travel to Wick. This prompted the chairman of the Thurso Community Council to describe the CGH as 'trouble, trouble, trouble' since it was opened.[25]

Time has shown how great a medical asset is the CGH to the county, although its architectural merits, especially on that site, can be questioned. The range and quality of services it has offered to the people of Caithness are excellent and will continue to be so well into the next millenium. The contrast with the first hospitals in Caithness is dramatic.

The last administrative change, unlikely to be the final one if the previous history of the medical services is anything to go by, took place in 1994 when the Caithness and Sutherland NHS Trust came into being. Its senior personel were as follows.

Chairman:	G.S. Bruce
Chief Executive:	G.S. Buchanan
Medical Director:	W.G. Johnston
Nursing Director:	Janet B. Pinion
Personel Director:	I.D. McCracken
Contracts Manager:	J.E. Bogle
Financial Director:	J.M. Steven

This trust is responsible in Caithness for the Caithness General, Dunbar and the Town and County hospitals. Dunbar Hospital in 1998 continues to be run by GPs. It has 16 beds dealing mainly with long-term elderly patients and physiotherapy, X-ray and out-patient departments. The Town and County hospital has 20 beds and houses psycho-geriatric and geriatric patients.

The Staffing of the NHS Hospitals

Consultant Appointments

The first NHS consultant in Caithness was Mr A.N. Roxburgh who had been appointed county surgeon with the HIMS in 1937. He remained as consultant surgeon until 1967, thereby being the longest serving consultant in Caithness.

Alexander Noble (Alex) Roxburgh (Plate 29) was born near Cape-town, South Africa, but had his schooling at George Watson's College, Edinburgh and graduated MBChB at the University there in 1930. His

Plate 29. Mr Alexander Roxburgh (Reproduced by courtesy of Mrs Stella Roxburgh).

postgraduate training was at Leicester and at Edinburgh where he was a clinical tutor at the Royal Infirmary. After becoming a Fellow of the Royal College of Surgeons of Edinburgh, he was appointed to his post in Caithness and became a superb general surgeon with a surgical (and when necessary, obstetric) repertoire which few colleagues in larger centres could emulate. It is recalled that the first operation he was asked to perform on his arrival was on a dog, there being no veterinary surgeon at that time. On his first Christmas Eve, a radio message summoned him to the island of Stroma, the only information or instruction being to 'bring instruments.. After a rough crossing, during which he was very sea sick, he walked across the island to the light-house and dealt with a retained placenta.[26] His workload, especially in the war years, was immense, and he tackled this entirely on his own. The award of an OBE in 1952 was popular and well merited. An athlete in his youth (tennis and squash were his games) he had a dislike of pretension and pomposity in any form – and was capable of puncturing both when he encoutered them. After his retirement he lived in Inverness until his death in 1991. Caithnessians should know that his work in the county is recognised in the naming of Roxburgh Street in Wick. The family association with medicine has been continued by his son, David who became a consultant radiologist at Stirling and Falkirk Infirmaries.

Before the advent of the CCH the non-surgical work of the Bignold hospital was done by the local GPs and some of these, along with Mr Roxburgh, Dr Minto as district hospitals officer, Miss Forbes, matron and nursing and ancillary staff, are seen in a group photograph of around 1963. (Plate 30).

Alex Roxburgh's successor was Mr Hugh Crum. Hugh Crum qualified in Glasgow in 1944, becoming a Fellow of the Royal Faculty of Physicians and Surgeons there in 1949. He trained and worked in thoracic surgery at Woodend Hospital, Aberdeen, and before his appointment to Caithness was surgeon at Huntly. He brought new surgical expertise to the county, especially in the use of endoscopic investigation. A keen Rotarian and gifted musician, he retired in 1986.

During the 1970s the surgical workload increased to the extent that a second consultant surgical post for the county became imperative. In 1980 Mr Pradip Datta from the Royal Shrewsbury Hosptial, was appointed. After Mr Crum's retirement there was some dubiety as to whether he would be replaced and it was even suggested that the surgeon at Golspie could assist paticularly with regard to performing endoscopies.[27] However, there was strong support for his replacement

Plate 30. Staff of Bignold Hospital (circa 1963). Back row: Dr J. Sutherland (GP), Dr Smith (GP), Mr Roxburgh (surgeon), Dr J. McAulay (GP). Middle row: Mrs Kidd (secretary), Mrs Richards (secretary), Sister Miller, Sister Taylor, Sister McBeth, ? Front row: Mrs Brown (physiotherapist), Dr Brown (GP/anesthetist), Miss Forbes (matron), Dr Minto (MOH), Sister Leith (Reproduced by courtesy of Miss Mary Sutherland).

and in 1987, Mr W. Johnston took up duties as consultant surgeon. He had had a career in the Royal Army Medical Corps and risen to the rank of Colonel, bringing expertise in urology and the surgery of trauma to the county. He now acts as medical director to the Caithness and Sutherland NHS Trust. Subsequently a third surgeon, Mr Paul Fisher was appointed.

The first consultant physician, appointed in 1964, was Dr D.H.A. Boyd, the present writer. He left to return to Edinburgh in 1970. There he latterly held the posts of consultant physician at the Western General hospital, Edinburgh and Leith hospital and honorary senior lecturer in the department of medicine, University of Edinburgh.

He was succeeded by Dr P.D. Robertson who had qualified in Aberdeen in 1954. After postgraduate training in the USA, where he worked in the department of internal medicine at the University of Iowa, he became FRCPE in 1978. Before coming to Caithness he was a senior lecturer in community medicine, at Edinburgh, with an interest in multiple screening and diabetic care. For his 25 years' work in Caithness and his work on various national committees, particularly his services to the Children's Panel network in the Highlands, he was awarded an OBE. He was joined in 1988 by Dr Timothy Shallcross and succeeded by Dr Schockran Ali Khan.

The first consultant obstetrician and gynaecologist was appointed in 1966. Dr Keith Laing, an Aberdonian, graduated there in 1958 and became a Fellow of the Royal College of Obstetricians and Gynaecologists. Before he was appointed he had had a distinguished army career and as a territorial had commanded a Field Ambulance for which he was awarded the Territorial Decoration (TD). His untimely death in 1979 at the age of 49 was widely mourned as he had worked hard and effectively to establish a first-class obstetric sevice in the county. He had retained a close connection with the medical school at Dundee but entered into the life of the local community in many ways, being associated as Chairman of the Thurso Lifeboat Committee and Scrabster Harbour Trust.[28] He was succeeded by Dr Ian Farquhar who was later joined by Dr Sebastian Borges.

As already mentioned, anaesthetics were given for decades by local general practitioners. In 1983 the first consultant anaesthetist, Dr Maria Cafferty, was appointed and since then Dr Isobel McKenzie, Dr Antonios Wagid and Dr Tom Collingbridge.

In 1996 a consultant psychiatrist, Dr Steven Walsh, was appointed who has care of the psycho-geriatric unit at the Town and County hospital. This was the last hospital service to be catered for adequately in the north. Craig Dunain, the psychiatric hospital in Inverness is of relatively recent origin. At the beginning of the century those who were referred to as the 'Parochial Insane' from Caithness were sent to Montrose Royal Asylum which must have meant virtual banishment for many poor families. There are records of others being sent to Morningside and Sunnyside Asylums.[29]

Over many decades, before and after the advent of the NHS, consultants and specialists not based in the county but visiting to conduct out-patient clinics in their own discipline, made a very substantial contribution to medicine in Caithness. These doctors had their main responsibilites in the Inverness hospitals. Initially physicians and gynaecologists did clinics but after the appointment of such specialists to Caithness, this practice ceased. Others continued and included orthopaedic and ENT surgeons, dermatologists and more recently, rheumatologists and chest physicians. Radiologists conducted diagnostic sessions mainly with regard to barium examinations. Ophthalmologists also attended and from 1950 until his retirement Dr Ian Georgeson saw ophthalmic patients at the Bignold hospital. Dr Georgeson was a member of a well-known[30] Caithness family, other members of which served the legal profession in Wick for many years.

Junior Hospital Doctors and General Practioners

A junior doctor of house officer (HO) grade was appointed to the Bignold hospital at Lybster on a temporary basis in the 1940s. Only with the appointment of a consultant physician were house officers appointed regularly. The first, in 1966, Dr John Rawles, a senior house officer (SHO) and a University College, London, graduate did much to assist in the establshment of acute specialist medical services. He eventually became a consultant physician and a senior lecturer in medicine at Aberdeen University. Thereafter HOs and SHOs in medicine were appointed regularly, and in surgery appointees were usually in registrar grade. With the establishment of the CGH the junior grade complements were rationalised at four medical SHOs and four surgical SHOs. Obstetrics has not had an establishment of junior hospital grades.

Although with developing specialist services GPs did not have the responsibility for patient care within the various units, they continued to play a part in the hospital scene, particularly for anaesthetics. In Thurso at the Dunbar hospital, Dr Ramsay Burnett gave anaesthetics for many years, as did Dr Brown, Dr Ian Burns and Dr John Eaton Turner at the Bignold. Dr Burns continued this task with the advent of the CGH where he also offerred expertise in neonatology, the care of the new-born. But when the work of the Central Hospital increased GPs also assisted in the running of follow-up clinics such as anti-coagulant clinics and diabetic clinics in which Dr Paul had a particular interest.

Nursing and Ancillary Staff

The matrons of the Caithness hospitals continued for the main part in their posts after the NHS. When the Central hospital opened Miss May Sutherland took on the responsibility for it as well as the Bignold. This was a difficult task and she was helped by the appointment of Miss Nita Barker as sister at the Central who set her own high standards of nursing in the new unit. Matrons, of course, disappeared and Senior Nursing

Plate 31. Dr P.D. Robertson, consultant physician, makes a presentation to Mr Peter Cowell, radiographer, on his retirement.

Officers and Directors of Nursing Services appeared. These are listed in Appendix 3.

Physiotherapy, in the person of the 'masseur' or 'masseuse' was represented at an early date in Caithness hospitals. In 1948 Miss Kerr was appointed as physiotherapist for the Bignold and Wick district but it was suggested she take 'a short course in radiography' which was agreed.*[31] Miss Robertson fulfilled the same role in Thurso. Not long after this when another physiotherapist was being appointed it is surprising to find that medical staff had a 'gender' problem indicating they thought 'a male physiotherapist not desirable.[32] Later, a male physiotherapist was appointed and now the CGH has a well staffed and equipped department.

Although the disadvantages of not having a trained radiographer were recognised and despite approval for the appointment of one being given in 1951, repeated advertising did not rectify this, although some short-term appointments were made. But in 1964 Mr Peter Cowell was

---

*The taking of X-rays was a task not infrequently undertaken by senior nursing staff as well.

appointed to the Bignold and when he retired in 1990 he was senior radiographer at CGH; he had a clear claim to be the longest serving person in this discipline in Caithness. He is seen on his retirement with Dr P.D. Robertson in Plate 31. Like the physiotherapy department the present radiology department is well staffed and equipped and vastly different from the first tentative beginnings in 1918.

Laboratory services in Caithness, as has been recorded did not begin until 1966 when the Central hospital came into being and the first laboratory technician (SMLT Grade 1) was appointed. Mr H.C. Wilson, the first incumbent set an admirably high standard. He was followed in 1969 by Mr Jack Urquhart, in turn succeeded by Mr Ernest Jones, principle MLSO in 1972. Under Mr Jones the Caithness laboratory became one of the most efficient and innovative parts of the hospital, contributing greatly to diagnosis and patient care.

Two pharmacists now staff the CGH pharmacy and other services such as occupational therapy are appropriately represented.

CHAPTER TEN

General Practice Since the NHS

THE INTRODUCTION OF THE NHS in 1948 allowed the implementation of changes, many of which had been suggested in previous reports, particularly that of the Royal College of Physicians of Edinburgh a century earlier. The extension of changes brought about by the Dewar report and the HIMS still did not ensure a medical paradise, although their benefits to the patients, and in many respects to the doctors were freely acknowledged.

Medical practice had been a fruitful field for reports over the years. These were and are usually lengthy, must be costly and sometimes contain apposite suggestions. The second half of the twentieth century has been no exception with the publication in 1967 of 'General Medical Services in the Highlands and Islands' (The Birsay Report). It dwelt mainly on general practice but also made some pertinent socio-economic comments, such as the importance of taking decisions for the Highlands and Islands in the area; the need for economic development if the population was not to continue to decline; and emphasis on the importance of rail services on medical and social grounds.[1] As regards population it pointed out that Caithness in 1961 had 66.6 per cent of its maximum population (in 1861) whereas Sutherland had only 52.4 per cent of its maximum. Caithness was the only county in the area which in the decade 1951–61 had a net gain in population; all others had net losses.

In a historical introduction the Birsay report refers to yet another report (Report of the Committee on Scottish Health Services (1936) – the Cathcart Committee) which noted a great improvement in the health of the people since the time of the Dewar report and the inception of the HIMS but recommended additional development of hospital and air ambulance sevices. It is also recorded that the minimum income of general practitioners in the HIMS was £800 in 1947, the last year of the scheme.[2]

In its chapter on the role and deployment of general practitiioners the Birsay report reveals that in 1966 Caithness had 57 principals per

100,000 population in general practice as opposed to 48 for the whole of Scotland. This was the lowest of any of the crofter counties and a marked contrast to Sutherland which had 105, reflecting a sparser, more scattered population with larger areas to be covered.[3] In actual numbers this translated into fifteen principals in Caithness, all male, with only two assistants and no trainees. The report did not consider that the medical manpower in the population of the Highlands and Islands was disproportionately high.

Sometimes local and national concepts of what was appropriate in medical cover did not coincide. The Scottish Medical Practices Committee considered that Wick in 1950 was under-doctored, but noted that there were no local complaints.[4] The Local Health Committee did not agree that the town was under-doctored but this prompted a letter in the press from a Sutherland doctor criticising Wick doctors for saying they could look after 3,500 patients each and covering a fairly large area.[5] Thirty years later it was still being said that Wick was the only place in the the Highland Health Board area that did not have enough GPs.[6]

Some perspicacious comments were made in the Birsay report about conditions of service, one of the most important perhaps being:

> Prolonged stay in a very small rural practice may not be in the best interests of the doctor or his patients. Favourable consideration should be given to doctors who are serving in remote areas when more central practices become vacant.[7]

Recommendations were also made about the grouping of practices to ease the burden of continuous personal responsibility of single-handed doctors and that where the work load permitted GPs should have responsibility for an element of public health and school medical examination work. It also recommended that GPs should to an increasing extent work in hospital. Those working three decades after this report can judge to what extent the recommendations have had an effect.

General Practice Premises

General practitioners in the 19th and early 20th centuries worked in the main from their own homes. Some had converted rooms or specially built annexes from which to work and consult. Not until the advent of the NHS were buildings designed to meet all the professional needs of GPs away from their homes. Some of these housed more than one practice and were, as might be expected, in the towns.

Plate 32. Opening of Thurso Medical Centre by Ex-provost John Sinclair, Lord-Lieutenant of Caithness.

In 1969 a medical centre was opened in Thurso.[8] Three practices involving seven doctors were accommodated there, the cost of the project being £19,000. The formal opening was by the Lord Lieutenant of Caithness, Mr John Sinclair who paid tribute to Provost Sutherland, a general practitioner in the town, who had originally proposed the centre[9] (Plate 32).

In 1965 the Board of Management of Caithness Hospitals, acting as Trustees of the Endowment Fund, agreed to make available from the remaining ground at the Henderson Memorial hospital, an area for use by local doctors to build a GP consulting centre.[10] The GPs concerned were not at that time willing to pursue such a scheme but it was revived a year later when a further meeting took place. On this occasion finance was to be obtained from central funds and the cost recovered from the GPs who used it.[11] This project went ahead, and in 1971 Wick's first medical centre was opened at Rosebank adjacent to the Central hospital. Those who applied to use it were Drs. Turner, Burns and Reid.[12] These premises functioned well for many years but became inconvenient because of lack of space, particularly for consulting rooms and offices.

So it was that the latest building to serve the medical needs of the people in Caithness came about. Opened in 1995 the new Wick medical centre on its excellent riverside site is a 'state of the art' building providing primary and community care under one roof. Ten consulting

Plate 33. Dr John Turner and Dr Emily Cobb open Wick's new medical centre.

rooms, a good reception area, ample office space and a medical library and meeting room are housed in a well designed building, the architects being Renwick Associates of Wick. There is, very imaginatively, a historical feature incorporated into the main entrance of the building – two stone arches from the former Wick Mart. Perhaps the influence of the Wick Project and the Highlands and Islands Enterprise can be seen in this. Mention has been made in previous chapters of the cost of some other medical buildings in Caithness in the past: it puts modern financial matters into perspective to record that this project cost £700,000.

The family doctors using this centre were Dr Millard, who played a leading role in its development, and Drs Douglas Paul, Ian Burns, Iain Johnston and Maurice Pearson.[13] But it was entirely fitting that one of the longest serving, retired GPs along with the latest should perform the opening ceremony. Dr John Turner and Dr Emily Cobb are seen, with some of the other GPs using the centre, at this task in Plate 33.

The Practitioners

The principals, (as opposed to the assistants, locums or trainees) who have worked in Caithness since the start of the NHS are listed in Appendix 4. Those who were in post at the start have now retired or, sadly, died. In Canisbay, Dr John Gill, who was appointed in 1940, served that community and the island of Stroma, on which he was more

143

than once storm-bound, until 1968. John Gill exuded dependability and was held in high regard by his patients. On his retiral his service to them was recognised but also his service to the Pentland United Football Club of which he was an avid supporter.[14] Dr J.G. McGregor, Castletown, who had graduated in 1906, was a Justice of the Peace and at one time had been a medical officer at the General Hospital, Singapore. He served only a few years in the NHS before his retirement but his son, Dr J.C. McGregor who qualified in Aberdeen in 1934, practised in Thurso until his retirement. John McGregor was a Squadron Leader in the RAFVR Medical Branch, and served throughout the 1939–45 War. Later, he undertook many arduous committee and administrative duties within the general practice scene in the county. Another Castletown practitioner left to pursue a distinguished academic career in occupational medicine. Dr William Taylor had Thurso connections and initially graduated BSc and PhD in chemistry, and worked for eight years with ICI (Imperial Chemical Industries). Deciding that he wished a change of career he studied medicine and qualified MB in 1950, subsequently holding hospital appointments and doing eight years as a single-handed GP. He left to achieve a second doctorate (MD with commendation) at Edinburgh and enter the department of occupational medicine at Dundee, becoming professor and deputy dean of post graduate medicine.[15] His special areas of interest, on which he wrote several papers, were the effects of noise and vibration and the toxicology of mercury. In retirement he returned to Caithness and from his home in Watten continued to take an enthusiastic interest in postgraduate medical matters in the county and world wide.

The first NHS practitioner in Dunbeath was Dr Ian Phillips who had graduated in 1942 and was soon on active service as an RAMC officer. He was in charge of surgical wards in Normandy after the D day landings, and was one of the first to use penicillin in infected war wounds. In Halkirk, Dr Angus Mackay saw in the NHS and served it and his patients for thirty years with constant support from his wife, Hope, also a doctor. He was a familiar, imposing, frequently kilted figure, a keen appreciator of good piping (he played the chanter), malt whisky and books. He was first chairman of the Northern Medical Committee and outside his professional work played an important part in organising the Halkirk Games.[16] His esteem was such that an Angus Mackay Memorial Fund was established and in 1981 it was able to provide an 'Ambulift' apparatus to Bignold hospital and a portable ECG machine to the Halkirk practice.[17]

Lybster was fortunate in having as its first NHS practitioner Dr J.L. McAulay who had qualified in Glasgow in 1925. His 36 year service to the community must rank among the longest in recent times. John McAulay was the epitome of the old GP yet was, to his retirement, receptive of the new and innovative and took pleasure in the improvements that advances in medicine and improvement in social conditions brought. He recorded that when he first came to Lybster '85 per cent of women of child-bearing age had mild if not severe rickets and confinements were difficult and prolonged' [due to pelvic deformities]. By the time of his retiral he considered this percentage to be two.[18] He was awarded an MBE in 1965 and retired to New Zealand.

The family doctor whose career spanned the last years of the HIMS in Thurso was Dr W.I.A. Fell. Ian Fell, an Aberdeen graduate of 1930, spent some time as a ship's doctor with the P & O line and also as RMO to the Hertford British hospital in Paris. His medical authorship implied he was proficient in French as he had an article published in the *Bulletine de la Société Chirurgiens de Paris*, an achievement not equalled by many British doctors. His somewhat conventional hobbies of fishing, shooting and bridge were off-set by the unusual one, for a doctor, of amateur dramatics at which he excelled.[19]

Ronald Sutherland, after war service, practised in Thurso but also worked for the local community in local government and eventually, as has been recorded, was honoured by being elected Provost of Thurso. Dr Ramsay Burnett was one of the Thurso GPs who administered anaesthetics at the Dunbar hospital for many years. Dr James Deans had duties outwith his Thurso NHS practice at the Admiralty Reactor Training Establishment, taking a special interest in diving and nuclear medicine. The discipline of public health attracted Dr Walter Geddes from practice in Thurso after only eight years. He took his Diploma in Public Health, became an MOH in Aberdeenshire and then Senior Medical Officer with Grampian Health Board.[20]

In Wick, the practitioners whose careers stretched into the NHS were Dr R.H.B McCrae and Dr W.H.B. Ramsay with Dr James Leask succeeding his father just before the start of the NHS. Dr D.G. Brown and later, Dr Ian Burns and Dr John Turner were among those who gave anaesthetics at the Bignold hospital for decades before specialist anaesthetists were appointed. Dr Turner who is pictured at the opening of the new Wick Medical Centre in 1995, sadly died in 1996. He had served in the Royal Navy and continued his interest in the sea, by holiday sailing and acting as lifeboat doctor. He was a veteran sports car enthusiast and was never seen far from an Aston Martin. Dr Burns' expertise in anaesthetics and the problems of the newborn has been recognised by his appointment in 1966 as hospital practitioner in paediatrics and occasional consultant anaesthetist. On leaving Caithness Dr Melville joined the National Coal Board as a medical officer but subsequently returned to general practice. Dr Reid left to further an interest in occupational medicine with ICI and later became senior medical officer with Boots Pharmaceuticals.[21]

The doctors recorded above and in Appendix 4 are greatly outnumbered by those who were born and educated in Caithness but who subsequently spent their professional lives in other parts of Britain or overseas. Some became distinguished GPs, others achieved national and international recognition in specialist and academic fields. During this century the number of men and women from Caithness who have contributed to medicine and been part of a medical diaspora must be very great. Some of these are recorded in the next chapter.

CHAPTER ELEVEN

The Public and Community Health in the Past 50 Years — A Miscellany —

THE SECOND HALF OF THE 20TH CENTURY has witnessed a continuing decline in many of the diseases, especially infections, which plagued our forebears. On the other hand there has been a rise in the incidence of diseases which were of no great importance or unknown to them.

After the Second World War there is no record of smallpox in Caithness and it was eradicated world-wide in the 1970s. Would our predecessors have thought this possible? From 1947 to 1951 epidemics of poliomyelitis (infantile paralysis) occurred in many countries but Caithness did not suffer greatly, only four cases being reported in the county in 1950. Of these, three were referred to the Orthopaedic Department at Raigmore hospital, Inverness.[1] In the report of the MOH for Caithness of 1956, vaccination against this condition was reported to be available for the first time. Dr Minto, the MOH, expressed disappointment at the unenthusiastic response; only 13 per cent of children in the appropriate age group had been registered and he explained this on the low incidence of the disease and therefore no sense of urgency among the population.[2] However, in a further two years good progress had been made and now poliomyelitis is largely confined to underdeveloped countries.

The Special Problem of Tuberculosis

Although the incidence and mortality of tuberculosis in Britain had been falling since the last century, the reasons for this being improvement in social and working conditions, housing and nutrition, the effects of world wars temporarily reversed these trends, and Caithness was no exception. The county MOH reported in 1949 that the standard of health was high except for the incidence of pulmonary tuberculosis.[3] The previous year had seen 32 cases of tuberculosis notified with 10 deaths.[4] The matter was taken up by the local Member of Parliament, Sir David Robertson, who asked a question in the House as to why there were 50 people with tuberculosis in Caithness awaiting admission for hospital treatment but only 10 beds available in the Town and County hospital. An English MP's response was the question, 'Why not send them to Switzerland?'[5]

There were, of course, two factors instrumental in causing the rapid decline in incidence and mortality of human tuberculosis after the Second World War, and making various forms of surgical treatment and the provision of 'sanitorium' beds unnecessary.* They were the advent of effective chemotherapy in the late 1940s, and immunisation by BCG, first introduced into Britain in 1949. Streptomycin, the antibiotic first used against tuberculosis, was in 1951 supplied to the Town and County hospital by the Public Health Department but paid for by the hospital.[6] A further measure in the fight against tuberculosis was the Mass Miniature Radiography (MMR) campaign designed to identify unsuspected and possibly infectious cases in the community. Caithness organised its first MMR campaign in 1957. From 5 to 15 July that year a total of 7,861 people had their chests X-rayed. Eleven cases of active pulmonary tuberculosis were found, four of which were sputum positive, that is, were capable of spreading the disease to others. Twenty-five others had inactive tuberculosis requiring observation.[7] From time-to-time after this MMR units would visit communities. Such a unit visited Caithness again in 1971 and on this occasion the main group targeted was school teachers. In all, 1,416 people were X-rayed but only four cases of tuberculosis were found, all inactive.[8] Tuberculosis is no longer the feared disease it was, but unlike smallpox, it has not been eradicated, and given certain circumstances could return to plague us.

Other Health Problems

The Medical Officer of Health, such an innovative and important appointment of last century, is no longer with us and the annual reports on health statistics are not now produced as such. From some of the last annual reports we can have some idea of how health matters have changed in just under a century. The individual reports from the burghs of Wick and Thurso for 1966, for example, show that deaths are now predominantly from degenerative, ischaemic or arteriosclerotic heart disease, strokes and malignant diseases rather than infectious diseases.[9] Indeed, in Thurso in that year there were more deaths attributed to

*Bovine tuberculosis in humans often manifesting as disease of the lymph glands (the old scrofula) intestines or bones, largely disappeared as a result of controlling the disease in cattle.

accidents in the home than from infectious diseases.[10] In 1971 the infant mortality rate for the county was 17 per 1,000 births, in 1905 the figure was 96, and the causes of infant deaths are now related more to congenital malformations than infections. The other welcome statistic of this year was the absence of maternal deaths which is certainly related to a hospital confinement rate of 99.48 per cent with only one domiciliary confinement.

The consequence of the general improvement in health and social conditions is that people are living longer and with families less able to look after infirm elderly relations and the chronic aged sick, the problem is a community one. In the past the Poor Law Institutions in Halkirk and Latheron were the only ones to which some sections of society had recourse. In 1950 Caithness Public Health Committee recognised the inadequacy of the accommodation for the care of the aged sick in the county and explored the possibility of increasing available beds in Forse House.[11] Under the terms of the National Assistance Act 1948, 40 beds were made available for this purpose and since that date 10 beds had been allocated to the Northern Regional Hospital Board. In 1963 conversion of one of the buildings at the Town and County hospital created a ten-bedded unit for chronic sick and six years later 26 beds for the elderly infirm were provided by Caithness County Council in a newly refurbished Pultney House in Wick. This house had been originally built by the British Fisheries Society in 1820 for its officials while Pultneytown was being constructed. It was fitting that the official opening was carried out by Dr R.H.B. McRae, a retired GP of Wick and Pultneytown.[12] Twenty-seven years on, a newspaper report[13] of the threat of closure of this home brings apprehension and sadness to many but the private sector is now providing old folks' accommodation in many places across the country.

The MOH was also responsible, through the child welfare clinics, for continuing nutritional policies during the Second World War. In 1948 in Caithness such baby foods as National Dried Milk, 'Virol' and 'Farex' as well as orange juice and cod-liver oil were supplied. The present day concern with nutrition is with health education and the attempt to persuade children and adults alike to eat a healthy diet. Long gone is the threat of actual famine which once overhung Caithnessians and with an increasingly common culture in these islands, nutritional habits and deficiences tend to be uniform. There has been no recent assessment of nutrition in Caithness, but in 1940 the Medical Research Council inquired into family diets in the Highlands and Islands. It made comparisons with families in other parts of the United Kingdom and concluded that the amount of protein, fat and carbohydrate consumed in the Highlands was superior to those in, for example, St Andrews, Cardiff and Reading. The intake of minerals and vitamins was judged to be 'sufficient' but the consumption of leafy vegetables 'low'.[14]

Dounreay and Health Hazards

There is seldom an innovation in human activity, intended and recognised as beneficial, which has not ultimately had disadvantages of some kind. The building of Dounreay Experimental Reactor Establishment in Caithness has had undoubted socio-economic benefits in the county and elsewhere. The decision to locate Britain's first fast-breeder reactor on this remote northern coastline was made in 1954 and the reason for this must imply the potential for some type of hazard involving ionising radiation. No overt dangers were encountered or suggested in the first decades of its existence and as has been described, the medical division of the plant assisted with the diagnostic use of medical isotopes at Caithness Central hospital in the 1960s. Nevertheless concerns about possible dangers to health began to be voiced, these being triggered by the reports of an increased incidence of childhood leukaemia around another atomic establishment at Sellafield. Reassurance came from the Chief MO to the United Kingdom Atomic Energy Authority (UKEA) who stated that deaths from leukaemia* in Caithness were average for the United Kingdom – about 5 per 100,000 population[15] – but doubts were reinforced by a letter to the *Lancet* in 1986 concerning childhood leukaemia in northern Scotland.[16] The matter received a public airing in the Town Hall, Thurso, in 1986, during proceedings for a planning application for a European demonstration fast reactor fuel reprocessing plant at Dounreay. Evidence was presented that there was no increase in congenital abnormalities or in cancer in general but that there was concern about the incidence of leukaemia in young persons around Dounreay. The latter problem has been the subject of several studies and papers. In 1987 a fuller report of the findings presented in the 1986 *Lancet* letter re-iterated a significantly increased incidence of leukaemia among young persons (0–24 years) in an area within 12.5 km round the reactor site between the years 1979–1984. Evidence at the time on the effects of environmental radiation did not provide an explanation for this.[17] No support was obtained for the

---

*A malignant disease of the white blood cells, one factor in the development of which is ionising radiation.

proposition that leukaemia and non-Hodgkins lymphoma in children near Dounreay is related to paternal occupation or to paternal exposure to external ionising radiation before conception. This particular study included 14 cases of leukaemia and non-Hodgkins lymphoma in children under 15 in Caithness between 1970 and 1986.[18] There have also been, of course, suggestions that these phenomena have an infective basis.[19]

Perhaps the most comprehensive report was that carried out by the Committee on Medical Aspects of Radiation in the Environment (COMARE) chaired by Professor Bobrow in 1988.[20] Among its conclusions, based on the same data as presented in 1987, were the statements that in the time period 1968–84 in an area within 25km of Dounreay six cases of leukaemia in people aged 0–24 were recorded; that all were in the final six year study period (1979–84), and that there was clear evidence of a significant excess of leukaemia in young people. A further conclusion was that, 'Reported discharges from Dounreay contribute only a small proportion of the total estimated dose from all forms of radiation, including natural background, medical radiation and nuclear weapons test fallout.' It goes on, '....some feature of the nuclear plants that we have examined leads to an increased risk of leukaemia in young people living in the vicinity of these plants. Conventional dose and risk estimates suggest that neither authorised nor accidental discharges could be responsible.' It admits, however, that there are 'uncertainties' about dose and risk calculations.

One wonders whether the uncertainties might have light shed on them following the release by the UKAEA in 1995 of reports of an explosion in a shaft containing radioactive material in 1977. This episode and matters relating to it are well described in an article in the *John O'Groat Journal* of 31 May 1996. It also lists an astonishing assortment of radioactive material which has been dumped in this shaft.

This is an ongoing and controversial matter which will be a health concern for citizens of Caithness for many years to come.

The People and Organisations concerned with Public and Occupational Health

The MOH for Caithness in post at the inception of the NHS was Dr R.F. McDonald. He had been appointed in 1946 following the long serving Dr Dick who continued as medical superintendent of the Bignold hospital after his retirement from the post of MOH. (Appendix 5) Dr McDonald remained in post only until 1948. He was succeeded by Dr A.F. McCoubrey and in 1952 Dr C.N. Minto, the last MOH for Caithness, was appointed. Charles Minto who qualified MBChB in Aberdeen in 1944, took his DPH in 1949. Before coming to Caithness he had worked at Culduthel hospital in Inverness and also as resident physician at a sanatoruim in St Johns, Newfoundland.

The assistants to the MOHs in this time were firstly Dr Helen Hood, who left in 1949. She was followed by Dr Doris McIntosh, wife of a local veterinary surgeon, who in turn was succeeded by Dr Vera Rugg, married to Mr Alex Rugg, farmer and one-time convenor of Caithness County Council. Vera Rugg, as did those assistants before her, acted as schools medical officer and worked also in general practice. She was one of those who responded to lifeboat emergencies, including some of a very hazardous nature. She had taken her DPH in 1948 and also her DTM&H (Diploma in Tropical Medicine and Hygiene) implying thoughts of practising overseas at one time. In 1974 Dr Minto, the last MOH, left Caithness.

The various duties of the county MOH since the first appointment in 1891 have been in large part described. Over the years he took on responsibilities in addition to his original ones. The Midwives Act of 1902 set up a register of professional midwives under the surveillance of the MOH. The School Service of 1907 encouraged the appointment of the MOH as principal school medical officer. Local authorities set up minor ailment clinics such as skin and ENT clinics as well as sanatoria, tuberculosis dispensaries and VD clinics with the help of the MOH. In the earlier days he was responsible for water supplies, sewage disposal, food hygiene, the public aspects of housing and the administration of the local authority hospital. With the NHS the MOH's lost their responsibility for hospitals and with the restructuring of the NHS in 1974 it became clear that there would be no place in a unified service for the MOH. He was replaced by the Community Medicine Specialist (employed by the NHS) whose function was to provide information to clinicians, to act as a manager in the planning of services and as an adviser to local authorities in public health matters. Environmental services however remained with the local authorities. The original sanitary inspectors, who became public health inspectors are now environmental health officers.[21]

Occupational health became an important issue in Caithness with the establishment of Dounreay because of the large number of people employed and the particular nature of the work carried out. Dr Maurice Hill was principal medical officer at DERE for many years. Other MOs involved in this organisation were Dr Douglas Wilson, Dr Norman Stott, Dr Gordon Morris and Dr R. Wood. Closely associated with DERE was the Admiralty Reactor Training Establishment (ARTE) which had almost 350 employees whose occupational health was supervised by a local practitioner, Dr Deans. The increase in population which the above organisations brought to the Thurso area was added to by a United States Navy establishment. The families of the servicemen were looked after by local GPs. The men had medical supervision from another base at Edzell.

Wick Radio

Although first thoughts do not associate Wick Radio with any aspects of medicine in Caithness, it has in fact a role with a medical clientèle far beyond the bounds of the county. Before the First World War the Admiralty established a wireless communications station at Wick to serve Royal Navy ships in the North Sea and North Atlantic. It was transferred to Post Office control in 1920 and for decades has given navigation warnings and dealt with distress calls from all shipping in the appropriate area.[22]

Part of this service was to give advice to ships' masters concerning medical emergencies experienced by their crew while at sea and without easy access to a port. This 'medico' service of the General Post Office was given free to ships of all nationalities through the twelve radio stations in the United Kingdom, of which Wick was one. In the eighth edition of a well-known textbook *Emergencies in Medical Practice,* published in 1967, the medical authorities for Wick Radio Station are given with telephone numbers and addresses as:

1. The MOH. (Dr C.N. Minto)
2. Alternative – The Assistant MOH. (Dr McIntosh.)
3. Or – The Resident Surgeon. (Mr A.N. Roxburgh)[23]

In practice, the radio station contacted by telephone any doctor who was available and willing to give advice. There would then follow a conversation, perhaps with the skipper of a Hull trawler somewhere off Iceland and advice given as to the best way of handling a medical problem in often difficult and worrying circumstances.

The Air Ambulance

Scotland's first air ambulance flight took place in 1933 from the island of Islay to Renfrew airport conveying a patient to a Glasgow hospital. The aircraft was owned by Midland and Scottish Air Ferries. Island to mainland flights have always been of greater importance than purely mainland flights and Highland Airways based at Inverness flew to Kirkwall via Wick before the Second World War. Orkney County Council had an agreement with this company for medical airlifts in 1934. Gander Dower's Aberdeen Airways (later renamed Allied Airways) ran regular flights to Shetland in 1936, the first medical flight on this route being in 1937. In that year an amalgamation of companies formed Scottish Airways which operated throughout the war until the creation of British European Airways in 1947. BEA aircraft for this purpose were Herons, Rapides, Heralds or Viscounts on occasionas but its successor, British Airways, withdrew Herons in 1973 and the ambulance role was taken over by Loganair, flying Islanders.[24]

When the first medical flights fromCaithness took place is not clear but it was not until 1946 that Caithness County Council took up the matter of an air ambulance service for the county with the Department of Health for Scotland (DHS).[25]

Among the arrangements there was provision that the service would be available to any patient in the county: that it would be used only when other means of transport were not available or suitable and only when local hospitals' facilities could not provide the treatment the patient urgently required: that where the patient was unable to afford the whole cost of conveyance, the cost borne by the patient would be determined by the County Council after consultation with the medical practitioner and the balance would be paid by the Council: that the DHS would be asked to repay to the Council two-thirds of the charge made by Scottish Airways: and that the Council would refund to the DHS one third of the charge for the nurse's services. These arrangements operated only for a relatively short time, as with the advent of the NHS the service was provided free of charge to patients.

The aircraft referred to are all fixed-wing craft implying the use of airports or landing strips. In 1955 the great value of helicopters was mentioned specifically by the MOH in his report.[26] This was the year of 'Operation Snowdrop' when a prolonged severe blizzard totally disrupted communication in northern Scotland and Caithness in particular. Six helicopters and and an Anson aircraft operated from Wick Airport dropping food and animal fodder to isolated farms and transporting medical and surgical patients from home to hospital and doctors to attend patients in their homes. People were instructed to mark a large cross in the snow if medical aid was required and a large 'C' if cattle fodder was wanted.[27] It is surprising therefore that fifteen years later the County Council favoured winged aircraft (with strategically placed landing strips) for an air-ambulance service. It was recognised that helicopters were very costly to operate and that only the armed forces could afford to do so.[28]

Although the air ambulance is still an essential service, its use sometimes prompts the question as to why the patient cannot be treated locally. For example, in 1987 a premature baby was flown from Wick to Aberdeen as Inverness airport was closed. The headline of a subsequent special article in the local press was 'Why babies must still fly south' – a question which was answered by the fact that the hospital did not have a consultant paediatrician. Nor could it, it was said, as the birth-rate was relatively low in Caithness and there would not be enough emergency cases to justify such an appointment.[29]

In 1990 the Scottish Ambulance Services air ambulance flew a patient with burns from Wick to Aberdeen. This was from Bond Helicopters (First Air-Ambulance) although normally Loganair would have been requested.[30] The service, like any other, has to evolve and be flexible.

Charities and Voluntary Work in the time of the NHS

It has already been shown how important was the local support for the voluntary and local authority hospitals in the years before 1948. The NHS did not diminish the rapport which Caithness people had with their hospitals, and donations, frequently in kind, continued to be made by individuals. Moreover, local organisations, clubs and societies raised money for specific purposes, often pieces of equipment not supplied by the NHS. Churches, Round Table, Rotarians, youth organisations are just a few examples of these generous bodies. In 1987 support for Caithness General hospital was put on a more organised basis by the formation of a League of Friends under the chairmanship of Mr Murray Banks[31] and there is a similar 'Friends of the Hospital' organisation in Thurso for Dunbar hospital.

Further evidence that voluntary organisations still play a part in supporting medical care in its broadest sense is the proliferation of societies founded to help the victims (and their relatives) of individual diseases. Epilepsy, diabetes, muscular dystrophy, alcoholism are but a few examples of conditions which have voluntary organisations with local branches to supplement and complement NHS care. The old benevolent, medical and nursing societies have, of course, long gone, but the International Red Cross through its local branches still provides first aid cover at a number of events and trains people in first aid. It also provides hospital services such as libraries and did so first to Caithness hospitals in the 1960s.

Caithness Doctors Furth of the County

To attempt to record these doctos who were born or educated in Caithness and who have spent their professional lives elsewhere is a difficult and of necessity, incomplete task. The following chronicles some of these from the second half of the century, the full record being beyond the scope of this book.

Janet Margaret Bisset (née Lamont), qualified in Edinburgh in 1949. She took her DCH in 1952 and became a Fellow of the Royal College of General Practice in 1976. She worked with her husband in general practice in Bolton but had been an assistant MOH in West Hartlepool. The family connection with medicine continues, with one of her sons a pathologist and the other a radiologist.[32] Her brother, Donald Lamont, has a long association with Wick and McKay's Hotel.

Ian Black. A native of Halkirk he graduated MA at Edinburgh University before the 1939–45 War, during which he served in the Fleet Air Arm. He qualified in medicine in 1951 and then emigrated to Canada where he specialised in pathology becoming a pathologist at Vancouver General Hospital and professor of pathology in the University of British Columbia. One of his areas of expertise was in the detection of cervical cancer.[33]

He was a grandson of Mr Gordon Dower, fishcurer of Wick, and one of a family which had strong representation in the medical profession.

Alexander Dower was the eldest son of the above Gordon Dower. He qualified MBChB in Edinburgh in 1921 and graduated MD (with Honours) in 1923. He was in general practice in Cardiff for 43 years, before retiring to the family home in Wick.[34]

Gordon Ewbank Dower. Another grandson of Gordon Dower, fishcurer (and presumably son of Alexander) he qualified MB in London in 1949 and also emigrated to Canada where he became an associate professor of pharmacology at the University of British Columbia. He is credited with developing, by the use of analogue computer, a type of cardiograph.[35]

William Calder. A native of Spinningdale but spent his childhood and youth in Caithness. He had an interest in psychiatry and took his Diploma in Psychological Medicine in 1949 after qualifying in 1933. He worked in general practice in Wick as an assistant to Dr Leask, then as a medical officer at Craig Dunain hospital, Inverness, but his main professional life was in HM Prison Service, of which he eventually became Principal Medical Officer. He wrote on the subject of sexual offenders.[36]

Ian Proctor Dunnet belonged to a well-known Caithness family but was one of those who helped forge the strong Caithness-Canada links. An Edinburgh graduate of 1949 he specialised in obstetrics and gynaecology taking the MRCOG and FRCS (Canada). He was on the staff of Vancouver General Hospital.

Duncan Alexander McKay Gillies. Born in Halkirk, the son of Revd Gillies, he graduated in science at Glasgow University and served as a radar Lieutenant in the Royal Navy during the war. He studied medicine and qualified in 1951 and later joined the staff of Craig Dunain hospital. He died at the early age of forty-seven.[37]

George John Green, a former pupil of Wick High School, graduated at Edinburgh in 1950. He went on to specialise in radiology, becoming consultant radiologist at Swansea. In addition to his radiological qualifications he was a Fellow of the Royal College of Physicians of Edinburgh.[38]

James Turner Gunn was a native of Latheron and proprietor of the Latheron estate. He graduated at Edinburgh in 1905 and became a Fellow of the Royal College of Surgeons of Edinburgh in 1908. During the First World War he served in the RAMC in India, but then opted for general practice in Auchterarder. Tragedy struck his family in the Second World War with the death of his younger son Alastair. As an RAF Flight Lieutenant he was shot by the Germans following the mass escape from Stalag Luft III in 1943.[39]

Bernard Mathieson specialised in psychiatry after graduating MB at Edinburgh in 1928 becoming physician superintendent and consultant psychiatrist at Smith Ockenden hospital and medical officer in the LCC Mental Hospitals Service. He was a native of Lybster.[40]

James Mowat from Keiss became a Fellow both of the Royal College of Surgeons of Edinburgh and of the Royal College of Physicians and Surgeons of Glasgow. His speciality was however obstetrics and gynaecology and he also became a Fellow of the Royal College of Obstetricians and Gynaecologists. The *'Groat'* reported his appointment as consultant obstetrician to the Royal Maternity hospital and the Victoria Infirmary, Glasgow and pointed out that he succeeded Sir Hector Maclennan. This reveals a further Caithness connection in that Sir Hector was the father of the present Member of Parliament Mr Robert Maclennan.[41]

Alexander Auld Miller. A son of Donald Miller of Durran he qualified in 1929, thereafter taking his MD, DTM, and DPH and eventually becoming senior consultant pathologist at the Royal Infirmary Preston. As a Lieutenant-Colonel in the RAMC he served in the East in the Second World War, publishing important work on severe outbreaks of infective hepatitis in Burma.[42]

James Galloway Shearer was the son of Mr Fred Shearer of Wick, and qualified in Edinburgh in 1941. He served in the RAMC in India and Burma and then went into general practice in Edinburgh. His other great interests were bridge and hockey.[43]

CHAPTER TWELVE

Epilogue

HOPEFULLY THIS ACCOUNT has given some idea of the changes in medical practice in Caithness from the time of the brochs to the era of Dounreay. Ignorance, fear and superstition gave little comfort to the early inhabitants of the county and primitive attempts at surgery and the administration of noxious and unpleasant medicines had to be endured for often dubious benefit. The years of scientific study into the structure and function of the body and the operation of the mind were slow in passing. The search for causes of disease and rational and effective means of dealing with them led often into blind alleys and frustration. But at last the application of science and technology has made possible therapeutic successes as never before and at the same time has not obliterated the humanity so necessary in good patient care.

Change, there has been, and the only certainty in the future is that change will continue. What this change will be is speculation but the challenge of predicting future innovations from today's medical growing points is irresistible. Indeed, a series of articles in recent editions of the British Medical Journal attempts just this. Not surprisingly the science of genetics figures prominently with 'Prospecting for gold in the human genome' as the striking title of the first article.[1] Genetic research, it points out, has produced an 'explosion of knowledge' and is leading us down unexpected paths. For example, recent discoveries with regard to what are now called 'substance use disorders' (drug abuse and alcoholism) relate to genetics and cellular mechanisms of drugs. Hypertension or high blood pressure (the commonest cause of strokes in this country) will have our understanding of it advanced only through molecular genetic analysis; and finally, a great deal of research is being done on using genetic material – gene therapy – in the treatment of malignant and infectious diseases.[2]

Our environment may become increasingly important to our physical well-being. Lung cancer is the most prevalent malignant disease in the Western world and is mainly caused by cigarette smoking. Yet only 20 per cent of smokers get lung cancer and the role of other environmental factors may be greater in the future. Prediction of climatic changes based on global warming have largely dealt with socio-economic factors but they can be made also in relation to diseases. A paper from the Department of Geography, University of Edinburgh studying temperature patterns in the past and possible increases in the future in south-east Scotland predicts that such conditions as Lyme disease and leptospirosis* will become more prevalent.[3] This is on the basis that insects and animals which can transmit disease to humans are likely to be more numerous in a warmer, wetter climate. If the warming and increased humidity is marked, it is not impossible that some diseases which were present at one time in the past in Britain may return. Malaria, transmitted by the anophiline mosquito is one. Arguments that malaria never occurred in Caithness have been presented but in the light of predicted climatic changes it may be rash to claim that it will never occur in the future. Some predictions of global warming however, indicate that paradoxically, the climate of Scotland may become wetter and colder in which case malaria would certainly not be a problem.

Apart from changes in disease patterns and advances in medicine, there is the problem of how medical services are to be delivered to the patient. There is no doubt that investigations and treatments are becoming much more costly and there has to be a realistic debate as to how they are to be paid for. The NHS has been one of the most enlightened social, political and medical projects of the century but many of its problems stem from chronic underfunding. The answer to proper and adequate funding in the future will have to be found or the basic concepts and aspirations of the NHS may be jeopardised which, in the opinion of one doctor who has spent a professional life-time in it, would be tragic. But what effect will the establishment of a Scottish parliament have on medical services? Perhaps little but the potential is there for innovations which may point to a surer and better managed future.

No matter what happens, however, it is certain that Caithness men and women will not only be served by the medical, nursing and ancillary professions, they will continue to play the important role they have always done in these professions.

---

*Lyme disease (named from Lyme in Connecticut where it was first described) is transmitted to humans by ticks. Leptospirosis icterohaemorrhagic (or Weil's disease) is contracted through contact with water contaminated by rat's urine.

Doctors listed in Mowat's Some Caithness Notables, *1928, and in his* A Bibliography of Caithness, *1940.*

From *Some Caithness Notables*

John Alexander., MD Durham, LRCP. MOH for Caithness. A benefactor of hospital and medical science. Born Watten 1839. Died Wick 1901.

David Anderson-Berry, MD, MS, FRS. A famous London physician. Born Wick, Son of Revd D. Berry. Afterwards added his mother's name.

Alexander Gunn Auld, MD, MRCP, Lond. Writer of several treatises on pathology. Editor of *London Medical Times.*

George Banks, JP, FRIPH, MOH, Wick. Local physician and surgeon for 60 years. Surgeon, Lt. Col. Caithness Volunteers. MO to Admiralty. Born Thurso 1835. Died Wick 1921.

W.T. Brock, DSc, MBCM, FRS. Authority on sanitation and public health. Native of Caithness.

James Cleghorn, MD, FRCS, CSI. Surgeon General Indian Medical Services. Hon. Surgeon to Queen Victoria. Born Wick.

James Grant, Lt. Col. VD. JP. LRCP&S. Orcadian medical practitioner. Born Latheron 1847. Died Stromness 1924.

Alexander Gunn. Eminent Edinburgh physician and surgeon. Worked with Lord Lister in the old Royal Infirmary of Edinburgh in connection with the famous scientist's antiseptic discoveries. Born Lybster 1844. Died Edinburgh 1914.

Robert Marcus Gunn, MB, FRCS. Surgeon, Royal Ophthalmic Hospital. London. Born Dunnet 1850. Died London 1909.

James Henderson of Clyth. Army surgeon and also medical practitioner in the north. Carried on herring fishing on Caithness coast. Born Clyth. Died Glasgow 1848.

William Henderson. Distinguished physician and Professor of General Pathology, University of Edinburgh. Pioneer on homeopathy. Born Thurso 1810. Died Edinburgh 1872.

John Sutherland Mackay, MD, DPH, MOH of Kirkcaldy and sugeon Rio Tinto Company, Spain. Born Lybster, son of Revd John Mackay. Died Edinburgh 1924.

William Mackay, FRCS. Celebrated physician in Spain. Brother of the above.

John Malcolm. Professor of Physiology in Dunedin University. Born Dunnet.

Aeneas Munro, MB, CM, FRFPS. Assistant Professor of Midwifery. Distinguished London physician. Pioneer of British nursing. Born Watten.

Andrew McGregor Sinclair. Mayor of Burnley 1915. Eminent public health administrator. Born Dunbeath.

Eric Suitherland Sinclair. Prominent local surgeon and pioneer Caithness ornithologist. Prepared an extensive collection illustrative of the natural history of the northern shires.

George Neil Stewart, MA, DSc, MD. Professor of Physiology Cleveland Medical College. Born Lybster.

John Frances Sutherland, MD, FRSE. Deputy Commissioner in Lunacy in Scotland. Specialist in mental disease and criminology. Born Lybster 1858. Died Tain 1911.

Peter Cormack Sutherland, MA, MD, FRGS. Surgeon-General of the Colony of Natal. Scientist, Arctic explorer, friend of Cecil Rhodes. Born Latheron 1822. Died Pietermaritzburg 1900.

In addition to these native Caithnessians he listed a few with more tenuous connection with the county. These included:

Dr William Gunn of Fatuna; a pioneer medical missionary in the New Hebrides; born in Helmsdale in 1853 but taught in Wick.

Miss Elizabeth MacDonald; first lady MD of St Andrews University and daughter of Donald MacDonald of Thurso.

Sir Eric Stevenson; eminent South African doctor, son of a daughter of Col. Sinclair of Forse.

Dr James Mill; chief magistrate of Thurso.

From *A Bibliography of Caithness*

D. Davidson, MD. LLD. Born in Wick, 1781. Died in Elie in 1858. He also had religious interests, writing a biblical dictionary.

George Finlayson. Surgeon and naturalist. Born in Thurso. In 1826 he wrote a *Journal of the Mission to Siam and Hue*.

James Innes, Surgeon of Thurso. Father of Lt. General J.J. McL. Innes RE, VC, CB, who wrote *The Sepoy Revolt*, 1897.

Robert Gordon MacDonald, MD Dunedin. Born Halkirk 1854. Died in 1931. He wrote a book with the intriguing title of *Thrift: the Secret of Making Money*.

William J. Sinclair, MD. He spent about a year in practice in Canisbay in 1885 but then entered the Prison Medical Service at Peterhead and Barlinnie. His only book had the exciting title *The Weather and the Climate of Peterhead*!

Halliday Sutherland, MD. Son of Dr J.F. Sutherland. Became a well-known and popular writer with books such as *Arches of the Years*.

M.A. Swanson, MB, Glasgow. A native of Bower. He wrote a pamphlet, 'Consumption – a Curable Disease'.

James L. Waters, MB. Born in Wick. Wrote *Celtic Life and Story*, 1911.

Lt. Col. George Waters, LRCP. Born in Olrig 1845. Died in Surrey 1933. He wrote reminiscences of his travels in 1932.

Pre-NHS Specialists and NHS Consultants in Caithness

Surgery

HIMS Appointments

	Appointed	Resigned/Died
Mr S.G. Davidson	1931	1934 (R)
Mr G.A.G. Mitchell	1934	1937 (R)
Mr A.N. Roxburgh	1937	–

NHS Consultants

	Appointed	Resigned/Died
Mr A.N. Roxburgh	1948	1967 (R)
Mr H.B. Crum	1967	1986 (R)
Mr Pradip Datta	1980	–
Mr W.G Johnston	1987	–
Mr Paul Fisher	1986	–

Medicine

NHS Consultants

	Appointed	Resigned/Died
Dr D.H.A. Boyd	1964	1970 (R)
Dr P.D. Robertson	1970	1995 (R)
Dr Timothy Shallcross	1988	–
Dr Ali Khan	1995	–

Obstetrics and Gynaecology

NHS Consultants

	Appointed	Resigned/Died
Dr Keith Laing	1966	1979 (D)
Dr Ian Farqhuar	1979	–
Dr Sebastian Borges	1994	–
(Associate specialist from 1989)		
Dr H. Olorunda	1997	–
(Long-term locum tenens)		

Anaesthetics

	Appointed	Resigned/Died
Dr Maria Cafferty	1984	1986 (R)
Dr Isobel Mackenzie	1987	1992 (R)
Dr Antonios Wagid	1986	1997
Dr T. Collingridge	1992	1997 (R)
Dr Gadiyar	1996	–
Dr R.N. Kumar	1997	–
Dr K.A. Abraham	1997	–
Dr I. Burns	1997	–
(Locum tenens)		

Psychiatry

	Appointed	Resigned/Died
Dr Steven Welsh	1996	–

Matrons and Senior Nursing Officers in Caithness

	Appointed	Resigned
Bignold Hospital		
Miss Paterson		1903 ?
Miss Sincalir	? 1916	?
Miss Janet Miller	1917	1919
Miss Aitken	1919	? 1929
Miss Bain MBE	? 1929	1949
Miss Margaret Campbell	1949	? 1960
Miss Forbes	? 1960	1965
Miss May Sutherland	1965	–
Bignold and Central Hospital		
Miss May Sutherland	1966	–
Dunbar Hospital		
Miss Marr	1920	1947
Miss Henderson	1947	1966
Miss Burgess	1966	?
Miss Cormack	?	?
Mrs Ness (SNO)	?	?
Mr Power(SNO)	?	–
Wick Combination Hospital		
Miss McGillivray	1892	–
Town and County Hospital		
Miss McGillivray	1910	?
Miss McLeod	?	?
Sister Sinclair} ?'acting	?	?
Sister Young} up'	?	?
Miss Stamp	1947	?
Miss Dinwoody (SNO)	1976	?
Mr McGiven (NPO)	?	?
Henderson Nursing Home		
Miss Begg	1928	1948
Miss Mowat	1948	1966
Caithness General Hospital		
Miss Sprott (Director of Nursing)	1987	–

Principals in General Practice from Inception of NHS

	Appointed	Retired Resigned/Died
Canisbay		
Dr J.P.B. Gill	1940	1968
Dr J. Donaldson	1968	1974
Dr W.D. Pyle	1975	1981
Dr C.R. Sharp	1982	1983
Dr I.D. Walters	1983	1984
Dr N.E. Fraser	1984	Present
Castletown		
Dr J.G. McGregor	1910	1952
Dr William Taylor	1952	1960
Dr J. Sutherland	1960	1990
Dr D. McNeill	1991	Present
Dr D.G. Robertson	1993	1997
Dunbeath		
Dr J.S. Phillips	1947	1964
Dr R.J.C. McBean	1964	1969
Dr D.G. Muirhead	1969	1993
Dr A Convery	1993	Present
Halkirk		
Dr Angus Mackay	1948	1979
Dr D.N. West	1980	1988
Dr G.R.M. Burnett	1988	Present
(Also practices Thurso)		
Lybster		
Dr J.L. McAulay	1930	1966
Dr I.G. Stewart	1966	1983
Dr P.A. Joiner	1983	Present
(Dr Angela Robertson.	1990	Present
Associate G.P. Lybster and Dunbeath)		
Thurso		
Dr W.I.A. Fell	1937	1962
Dr J.C. McGregor	1946	1977
Dr W.R.N. Sutherland	1947	1976

	Appointed	Retired Resigned/Died
Thurso (cont)		
Dr W. Geddes	1958	1966
Dr A.R. Burnett	1962	1983
Dr J.P. Deans	1962	1990
Dr Callum Mackay	1964	1992
Dr Norna Mackay	1965	1979
Dr P.M. McMorran	1976	1990
Dr R.T. Purcell	1974	1981
Dr D. Ramsay	1972	1983
Dr A.H.A. Robertson	1977	1984
Dr G.B. Birnie	1983	Present
Dr A.R. Muir	1983	1990
Dr G.A.A. Shepherd	1982	Present
Dr J.D. Morrison	1984	Present
Dr A.G. Brooks	1988	Present
Dr D.M. Cruikshank	1991	1994
Dr S.R. Findlay	1991	Present
Dr P. Christie	1995	1996
Dr E.L. Eccles	1994	1996
Dr M.L. MacDonald	1995	Present
Dr N.L. Harvey	1996	Present
Wick		
Dr W.H.B. Ramsay	1929	1960
Dr R.H.B. McCrae	1934	1964
Dr J.C. Leask	1946	1970
Dr Vera Rugg	1953	1963
Dr J.G. Smith	1964	1968
Dr D.G. Brown	1960	1964
Dr I.J. Burns	1964	1995
*Dr Elizabeth Finlayson	1966	1968
Dr J.M. Eaton Turner	1960	1990
Dr Alan Melville	1972	1975
Dr I. Johnstone	1975	Present
Dr D.W.T. Paul	1970	1996
Dr M.R. Pearson	1968	Present
Dr A.B. Reid	1970	1975
Dr P.J.M. Pearson	1981	1984
Dr E.R. Millard	1990	Present
Dr E.J. Cobb	1995	Present
Dr B.P. Cheesman	1996	Present
Dr L.J. Cheesman	1997	Present

* (Dr Finlayson has also done locum work in the county for many years)

Medical Officers of Health and Assistant MOHs, County of Caithness

MOHs	Appointed	Resigned/ Retired.
Dr John Alexander	1891	1901
Dr George Dick	1902	1946
Dr R.F. McDonald	1946	1948
Dr A.F. McCoubrey	1949	1952
Dr C.N. Minto	1952	1974
Assistant MOHs		
Dr Janet Bruce	1940	1943
Dr Janet Mowat	1943	1946
Dr Helen Hood	1946	1949
Dr Doris MacIntosh	1955	1963
Dr Vera Rugg	1963	1974

References

Chapter 1

1. Wickham-Jones C R. (1994) *Scotland's First Settlers*, p.11. London. Batsford.
2. Dickinson W C. (1961) *A New History of Scotland*, vol. 1. p.15 Edinburgh: Nelson.
3. Piggott S. (1982) *Scotland Before History*, Edinburgh University Press.
4. Omand D. (ed.) (1972) *The Caithness Book*, p.102. Inverness: Highland Printers.
5. Wickham-Jones C R. *Op. cit.*, p. 23.
6. Omand D. *Op. cit.*, p. 102.
7. Piggott S. *Op. cit.*
8. Omand D. *Op. cit.*, p.106.
9. *Ibid.*, p.111.
10. *Ibid.*, p.119.
11. Diringer D & Olson D R. (1991) in *Encyclopaedia Britannica*, vol. 29. p.1048.
12. Guthrie D. (1958) *A History of Medicine*, pp. 5–10. London: Nelson.
13. Laing S. (1866) *Pre-Historic Remains of Caithness*, Edinburgh.
14. Corcoran J X W P. (1964–66) 'The Excavation of Three Chambered Cairns at Loch Calder, Caithness' pp.1–76, Proc. Soc. of Antiquaries of Scotland, vol XCVII.
15. Lunt, Dr Dorothy. Personal communication.
16. Little M. Personal communication.
17. Turner R C & Scaife R G. (1995) *Bog Bodies*. British Museum Press.
18. Beith Mary (1995) *Healing Threads*, p. 16. Edinburgh: Polygon.
19. Guthrie D. *Op. cit.*, p.10.
20. *Ibid.*, p.14.
21. Comrie J D. (1932) *History of Scottish Medicine*, vol. 1. p.30 London, Bailliere, Tindall & Cox.
22. *Ibid.*, p. 33.
23. *Ibid.*, p.38.
24. *Ibid.*, p. 41.
25. Beaton D. (1909) *The Ecclesiastical History of Caithness*, p.8. Wick.

Chapter 2

1. Johnston R B. *Place Names of Scotland* (1934), p.299. London: S R Publishers.
2. Omand D. (ed.) *The New Caithness Book* (1989), p. 139. Wick: North of Scotland Newspapers Ltd.
3. Beaton, Revd D. *The Ecclesiastical History of Caithness*, (1909) p. 60. Wick.
4. Johnston A W & A. (Ed.) *Caithness & Sutherland Records*, vol. 1. (1909), p. 30. London: Viking Society for Northern Research.
5. Omand D. *Op. cit.*, p.83.
6. Guthrie D. (1958) *A History of Medicine*, p.128 London: Nelson.
7. Omand D. *Op. cit.*, p.82.
8. Row J. (1842) *Historie of the Kirk in Scotland*, p. 342. The Maitland Club.
9. Comrie J D. (1932) *History of Scottish Medicine*, vol. 1 p. 58. London: Bailliere, Tindall & Cox.
10. Guthrie D. *Op. cit.*, p.107.
11. Moffat B. (1986) *First Report on Researches into the Mediaeval Hospital at Soutra, Lothian Region*, p. 32. Edinburgh : SHARP Practice.
12. Moffat B. (1988) *Second Report on Researches into the Mediaeval Hospital at Soutra, Lothian Region*, p. 14. Edinburgh: SHARP Practice.
13. Richards P. (1977) *The Mediaeval Leper*, p.4. Cambridge: Brewer.
14. Simpson J W. (1872) 'On Leprosy and Leper Hospitals in Scotland & England', in *Archealogical Essays*, vol. 2. ed. Stuart J. Edinburgh.
15. Richards P. *Op. cit.*, p. 83.
16. *Ibid.*, p.104.
17. Shrewsbury J F D. (1970) *A History of the Bubonic Plague in the British Isles*, p.37. Cambridge University Press.
18. Shrewsbury J F D. *Ibid.*, p.206.
19. Slade P. (1985) *The Impact of Plague in Tudor & Stuart England*, p.76. London: Routledge & Kegan Paul.
20. Slade P. *Ibid.*, p. 47.
21. Comrie J D. *Op. cit.*, p. 206.
22. *Ibid.*, p.93.
23. Beith Mary (1995) *Healing Threads*, p.51. Edinburgh: Polygon.
24. *Ibid.*, p.56.
25. Comrie J D. *Op. cit.*, pp 93 – 99.
26. Warrack J. (1920) *Domestic Life in Scotland 1488–1688*, p.129. London.

Chapter 3

1. Omand D. (ed.) (1972) *The Caithness Book*, p. 135. Inverness: Highland Printers.
2. Omand D. (ed.) (1989) *The New Caithness Book*, p. 99. Wick: North of Scotland Newspapers Ltd.
3. Hamilton D. (1981) *The Healers*, p.42. Edinburgh: Canongate.

4. Omand D. *Op. cit.*, p. 134.

5. Skinnner H A. (1961) *The Origin of Medical Terms* 2nd edn., p.12 Baltimore.

6. Smout T C. (1060) *History of the Scottish People 1560–1830*, p.253. London: Collins.

7. Brotherstone J H F. (1952) *The Early Public Health Movement in Scotland* London.

8. Price F W. (1946) *Textbook of the Practice of Medicine*, 7th edn., p.253. Oxford Medical Publications.

9. Ritchie J. (1920) *The Influence of Man on Animal Life in Scotland*, p.508. Cambridge University Press.

10. Duncan K. (1993) 'The Possible Influence of Climate on Historical Outbreaks of Malaria in Scotland' *Proc. R. College. Physicians Edinb.*, 23, 55.

11. Finlay M D L. (1978) 'An Enquiry into to the Ague in Scotland' p.177. Thesis for the degree of Doctor of Medicine, University of Edinburgh.

12. *Ibid.*, p. 180.

13. Rogers, Revd C. (1884) *Social Life in Scotland*, p. 135. Edinburgh.

14. Gilchrist E. (1771) 'Essays & Observations', *Philososphical Soc. Edinb.* 3, 154.

15. *Scottish National Dictionary.*

16. Cullen G.M. (1911) 'Concerning Sibbens & the Scottish Yaws', *Caledonian Med. J.*, 8. 36.

17. Morton R S. (1967) 'The Sibbens of Scotland', *Med. Hist.*, 2 , 374

18. Hibbert S. (1826) *Edin. J. med.* Sci., 1, 287

19. Gilchrist E. *Op. cit.*

20. Cullen G M. *Op. cit.*

21. Hutchison G H. (1896) *Arch. Sury.* 17, 23.

22. Hutchison G H. (1900) *Brit. med. J.*, 2, 561.

23. Calder J T. (1887) *History of Caithness*, Wick.

24. Parish Register of Canisbay, 1652–1666. Revd P. Beaton (ed.). (1914). Edinburgh: Scottish Records Office.

25. Canisbay Session Records, March 1652–February 1666. Transcribed by Morris Pottinger (1993) Wick Library.

26. Crofton J W. & Douglas A C. (19619) *Respiratory Diseases*, p. 163. Oxford Edinburgh:Blackwell.

27. Hamilton D. *Op. cit.*, p.78.

28. *Ibid.*, p.52.

29. *Ibid.*, p.58.

30. Foden F. (1996) *Wick of the North*, p.263. Wick: North of Scotland Newspapers Ltd.

31. Craig W S. (1976) *History of the Royal College of Edinburgh*, p.15. Oxford & Edinburgh: Blackwell.

32. Smout T C . *Op. cit.*, p. 189.

33. Hamilton D. *Op. cit.*, p. 80.

Chapter 4

1. Youngson A J. (1973) *After the Forty-five*, p.21. Edinburgh University Press.
2. Beaton, Revd D. (1909) *The Ecclesiastical History of Caithness*, p.2. Wick.
3. Fyfe J G. (Ed.) (1942) *Scottish Diaries and Memoirs 1746–1843*, Stirling.
4. Lang A. (Ed.) (1898) *The Highlands of Scotland in 1750*, Edinburgh.
5. Pennant T. (1979) *A Tour in Scotland*, Perth: Melven Press.
6. Donaldson J E. (1938) *Caithness in the Eighteenth Century*, p. 33. Edinburgh.
7. Bayne, Aneas. *A Short Geographical Survey of the County of Caithness, 1735*, transcribed by Morris Pottinger. 1993. Thurso: Reay.
8. Sinclair, Sir J. (Ed.) (1794) *The Statistical Account of Scotland: County of Caithness*, p.195.
9. *Ibid.*, p. 256.
10. Donaldson J E. (1984) *The Mey Letters*, Australia.
11. Henderson J. (1884) *Notes on Caithness Family History*, Edinburgh: David Douglas.
12. *Encyclopaedia Britannica*, 15th edn. (1991) vol. 10. p. 313.
13. Craig W S. (1976) *History of the Royal College of Physicians of Edinburgh*, p. 645. Edinburgh: Blackwell Scientific Publications.
14. Henderson J. *Op. cit.*, p. 195.
15. MacNaughton W A. (1897) *Medical Heroes of the 'Forty-five'*, Glasgow.
16. Van Strien K. (1995) 'A Medical Student at Leiden & Paris', *Proc. R. Coll. Physicians Edinb.*, 25, 294.
17. Streets Ms. Sheila. (1996) Personal Communication.
18. Sinclair of Freswick Papers. Scottish Record Office, 136/31
19. *Ibid.*, 136/1191
20. Calder J T. (1887) *History of Caithness*, p. 203. Wick.
21. Sage, Revd D. (1899) *Memorabilia Domestica: or Parish Life in the North of Scotland*, p.160. Wick: Wm. McRae.
22. Sinclair of Freswick Papers. Scotish Record Office, 136/1189/5–7.
23. *Ibid.*, 136/436/54.
24. *Ibid.*, 136/436/39.
25. *Ibid.*, 136/436/90.
26. *Ibid.*, 136/436/30.
27. *Ibid.*, 136/436/73.
28. *Ibid.*, 136/436/70.
29. *Ibid.*, 136/436/6.
30. *Ibid.*, 136/436/31.
31. *Ibid.*, 136/526.
32. *Ibid.*, 136/436/19.
33. Buchan W. (1791) *Domestic Medicine*, 12th edn. p.195 London.
34. Cullen William. (1791) *Practice of Physic*, p. 142. Edinburgh.
35. Sinclair, Sir J. *Op. cit.*, p. 170.

36. Sinclair of Freswick Papers, Scottish Record Office, 136/436/35.
37. The War Office. (1946) *Medical Diseases in Tropical and Sub-Tropical Areas*, 8th edn. p. 301. HMSO.
38. Sinclair of Freswick Papers, Scottish Record Office. GD/136/1200/1.
39. Miller J. (1990) 'Smallpox in the Highlands', *The Medical Post*: Toronto.
40. Pennant T. *Op. cit.*
41. Sinclair, Sir J. *Op. cit.*, p. 176.
42. Comrie J D. (1932) *History of Scottish Medicine*, vol. 1. p. 429. London: Bailliere, Tindall & Cox.
43. Craig W S. *Op. cit.*, p. 93.
44. Sinclair of Freswick Papers, Scottish Record Office, GD/136/1092.
45. Buchan W. *Op. cit.*, p. 154.
46. McKay of Bighouse Muniments, Scottish Record Office, GD/87/2
47. Quoted in: Rodgers EHB (1893) *Aberdeen Doctors*, p.175. Edinburgh; Blackwood.
48. Beith, Mary. (1995) *Healing Threads*, p. 27. Edinburgh: Polygon.

Chapter 5

1. Omand D. (Ed.) (1972). *The Caithness Book*, p. 218. Inverness.
2. Sinclair, Sir J. (Ed.) (1794) *The Statistical Account of Scotland: County of Caithness*, p.170.
3. Calder J T. (1887) *History of Caithness*, p. 230. Wick.
4. Beaton, Revd D. (1909) *The Ecclesiastical History of Caithness*, Wick.
5. Mowat W G. (1959) *The Story of Lybster*, Wick.
6. Report of a Committee of the Royal College of Physicians of Edinburgh (1850) 'Medical Practice in the Highlands'.
7. *Ibid.*, p.270.
8. *Ibid.*, p. 519.
9. Comrie J D. (1932) *History of Scottish Medicine*, vol. 11 p. 787. London: Bailliere, Tindall & Cox.
10. Guthrie D. (1958) *A History of Medicine*, 2nd edn. p. 378 London: Nelson.
11. Medical Directory for Scotland (1852) and onwards.
12. Mowat J. (1928) *Some Caithness Notables*, Wick.
13. Mowat J. (1940) *A Bibliography of Caithness*, Wick: Reid.
14. *John O'Groat Journal*, 10/2/1922.
15. Mowat J. *Op. cit.*
16. Logan Turner. (1929) *History of the Royal Infirmary of Edinburgh*, pp.240–241. Edinburgh: Oliver & Boyd.
17. *Lancet.* (1909) vol. 11. p.1786.
18. Mowat R I. (1992) *A Short Account of Proprietors, Inns & Alehouses in Latheron Parish 1750–1900s*, Lybster: Wick Public Library.
19. Comrie J D. *Op. cit.*, p. 623.
20. *John O'Groat Journal.* 26/8/1842.

21. *Ibid.*, 23/3/1838.
22. Calder J T. *Op. cit.*, p. 31.
23. *John O'Groat Journal*, 9/10/1931.
24. Burrows E H. (1958) *A History of Medicine in South Africa*, Capetown: Balkema. p.209.
25. Coghill, Ronald (1997). Personal Communication.
26. *John O'Groat Journal*, 1/7/1921.
27. Waters, Falconer (1974) *Thurso, Then & Now*, p. 14. Caithness Books.
28. *New Statistical Account of Scotland*, (1845).
29. *John O'Groat Journal*, 7/6/1836.
30. Banks J S. (1972) *The Heather Blooms at John o' Groats*, Wick.
31. Jenkinson J. (1993) *Scottish Medical Societies 1731–1939*, Edinburgh University Press.
32. Beith, Mary (1995) *Healing Threads*, p. 134. Edinburgh: Polygon.
33. Beaton, Revd D. *Op. cit.*, p. 8.
34. Beith, Mary *Op. cit.*, p. 103.
35. *Ibid.*, p. 197.
36. Lindsay, Helen. (1985) *Folklore of Dunbeath*, Dunbeath Preservation Trust.
37. *John O'Groat Journal.* 5/6/1914.
38. Beith, Mary. *Op. cit.*, p.160.
39. *John O'Groat Journal*, 6/4/1838.
40. *Ibid.*, 14/3/1844.
41. *Ibid.*, 20/10/1840.
42. McKay, Donald. (1965) 'This Was My Glen', Caithness Notebook No. 2.

Chapter 6

1. Comrie J D. (1932) *History of Scottish Medicine*, vol. 2. p. 611. London: Bailliere, Tindall & Cox.
2. Ferguson T. (1958) *Scottish Social Welfare 1864–1914*, p. 436. Edinburgh: Nelson
3. Pryde G S. (1962) *Scotland from 1603 to the Present Day*, p. 200 London: Nelson.
4. Ferguson T. (1948) *The Dawn of Scottish Social Welfare*, p. 249. Edinburgh: Nelson.
5. Ferguson T. (1958) *Op. cit.*, p. 3.
6. Minutes, Parochial Board of Latheron, 19/11/1849.
7. Minute Book, 1848. Wick Parochial Board.
8. Ferguson T. (1958) *Op. cit.*, p. 1.
9. *New Statistical Account of Scotland*, (1845) p. 121.
10. County of Caithness. Report by Medical Officer, 1892.
11. *Ibid.*, 1903.
12. Edwards C R W & Bouchier J A D. (Eds) (1991) *Davidson's Principles & Practice of Medicine*, 16th edn. p. 132. Edinburgh: Churchill-Livingstone.

13. Creighton C. (1891) *A History of Epidemics in Britain*, vol. 2. p. 813 Cambridge.
14. Ferguson T. (1948) *Op. cit.*, p. 127.
15. *John O'Groat Journal*, 23/8/1844.
16. Miller, Hugh. (1850) *My Schools and Schoolmasters*, p. 237. Edinburgh: Black.
17. *John O'Groat Journal*, 23/11/1849.
18. Minute Book 1850. Wick Parochial Board.
19. Bushnan J S. (1850) *Cholera & its Cures*, pp. 130–145 London: Orr.
20. Boyd D H A. (1990) *Leith Hospital 1848–1988*, p.6. Edinburgh: Scottish Academic Press.
21. Creighton C. *Op. cit.*, p. 855.
22. Stark (1865) 'Remarks of the Epidemic Fever of Scotland', *Transactions of the Epidemiological Society of London*. 11, 304.
23. Patrick A. (1955) *The Enteric Fevers 1800–1920*, Royal College of Physicians, Edinburgh.
24. Creighton C. *Op. cit.*, p. 211
25. Ferguson T. (1958) *Op. cit.*, p. 386.
26. Grant D. (1966) 'Old Thurso'. Caithness Notebooks No. 4.
27. *John O'Groat Journal*, 16/11/1838.
28. Minutes of the County District Committee of Caithness, 12/6/1890.
29. *Ibid.*, 8/10/1891.
30. *Northern Ensign*, 8/10/1901.
31. McKay D. (1965) 'This Was My Glen'. Caithness Notebooks No. 2.
32. County of Caithness, Report by Medical Officer, 1891.
33. *Ibid.*, 1900.
34. Craig W S. (1976) *History of the Royal College of Physicians of Edinburgh*, p.661. Edinburgh: Blackwells.
35. Obituary. *Brit. Med. J.* (1976) p. 1329.
36. County of Caithness, Report by Medical Officer, 1892.

Chapter 7

1. Comrie J D. (1932) *History of Scottish Medicine*, vol. 2: p.449. London: Bailliere.
2. Comrie J D. *Ibid.*, p. 450.
3. *John O'Groat Journal*, 1/7/1890.
4. *Ibid.*, 25/5/1920.
5. *Statistical Account of Scotland* (1794), vol. 18. p.176.
6. County of Caithness, Report by Medical Officer, 1896.
7. *Ibid.*, 1894.
8. *Ibid.*, 1902.
9. *John O'Groat Journal*, 15/3/1996.
10. County of Caithness, Report by Medical Officer, 1894.

11. *Ibid.*, 1903.

12. *Ibid.*, 1892.

13. Wick Combination Hospital. Regulations for the Internal Management. 1897.

14. *John O'Groat Journal*, 19/9/1910.

15. County of Caithness, Report by Medical Officer, 1911.

16. Glass N M (1994) 'Caithness & the War 1939–45' p. 23. Wick.

17. *John O'Groat Journal*, 26/4/96.

18. *Ibid.*, 15/3/1996.

19. *Ibid.*, 14/8/1936.

20. *The Northern Herald*, 16/7/1903.

21. *John O'Groat Journal*, 29/7/1910.

22. Bignold Cottage Hospital, Annual Report, 1916.

23. Bignold Hospital, Register & Admission Book, 1903–1904.

24. Reid M. (1987). *Ask Sir James*, p. 250. London.

25. *Bignold Cottage Hospital. Wick, NB. A Brief Story of its Activities*, (1929). London.

26. Minutes, Bignold Cottage Hospital Trustees, 14/12/1939.

27. *Ibid.*, 11/7/1940.

28. Bignold Hospital, Register & Admission Book, 1940.

29. Glass N M. *Op. cit.*, p.12.

30. Minutes, Bignold Cottage Hospital, 27/10/1940.

31. *Ibid.*, 21/11/40.

32. *Ibid.*, 13/2/41.

33. *Ibid.*, 9/10/41.

34. Sutherland, Miss May. Personal Communication. 1997.

35. Minutes, Bignold Cottage Hospital, 13/3/41.

36. *Ibid.*, 20/4/43.

37. *Ibid.*, 24/6/43.

38. *Ibid.*, 30/11/45.

39. *Ibid.*, 16/1/46.

40. *Ibid.*, 3/7/48.

41. Minute Book of the Wick & Pulteneytown District Nursing Association, 7/11/1927.

42. *John O'Groat Journal*, 21/7/1995.

43. Minute Book of the Wick & Pulteneytown Nursing Association, 7/12/1927.

44. *Ibid.*, 3/3/1928.

45. *Ibid.*, 12/4/1928.

46. *John O'Groat Journal*, 14/8/1931.

47. Minutes. Henderson Memorial Nursing Home, 11/6/1948.

48. *John O'Groat Journal*, 15/5/1914.

49. *Ibid.*, 18/12/1936.

50. *Ibid.*, 17/11/1848.
51. Jones, Peter. (1996) *Surgery in Aberdeen: Sixty Years of Change. 1847–1907*, p. 21. Aberdeen History of Medicine Publication.

Chapter 8

1. *John O'Groat Journal*, 6/9/1901.
2. *Ibid.*, 14/3/1902.
3. *Ibid.*, 20/10/1911.
4. Scottish Records Office, AF 42/2634.
5. *Ibid.*, AF 42/2533.
6. Comrie J D. (1932) *History of Scottish Medicine*, vol II p. 792. London: Bailliere, Tindell & Cox.
7. *Report & Minutes of Evidence: Highlands & Islands Medical Service Committee (1912)*, HMSO.
8. Simpson J B. (1938) 'Medical Practice in the Highlands During the Past Fifty Years', Ca. Med. J. p. 200.
9. Crossfell M L. *The Highlands & Islands Medical Service. A Dry Run for the NHS*.
10. Scottish Records Office, AF 43/40.
11. Cockcroft, Janet *Not a Proper Doctor*, p. 13.
12. Banks J S. *The Heather Blooms at John o' Groats*, p. 97.
13. *Ibid.*, p. 109.
14. *John O'Groat Journal*, 18/11/1910.
15. 'Times Gone By' (1991) 1935, p. 27. North of Scotland Newspapers, Wick.
16. Medical Officer's Report. Burgh of Thurso. 1936.
17. Medical Officer's Report. Burgh of Wick 1936.
18. Minute Book, Wick Parish Council 1925–30.
19. Boyd W. (1943) *Texbook of Pathology*, 4th edn. p.208. Kimpton: London.
20. Leask J. (1920) 'Observations upon the Influenza Epidemic as affecting the Eastern parts of Caithness, with Statistics', MD Thesis, University of Aberdeen.
21. Highlands & Islands Medical Services Committee Report (1912–13), Chapter 9. HMSO.
22. Ferguson T. (1958) *Scottish Social Welfare 1864–1914*, p. 457. Edinburgh.
23. *John O'Groat Journal*, 28/7/1893.
24. *Ibid.*, 24/3/1933.
25. *Ibid.*, 1/3/1901.
26. Smith J A. (ed.) (1988) *Third Statistical Account of Scotland: County of Caithness*, p. 40. Scottish Academic Press.
27. *John O'Groat Journal*, 22/1//1915.
28. *Ibid.*, 14/12/1951.
29. *Ibid.*, 9/4/1915.
30. Crofton, Eileen. (1997) *The Women of Royaumont*, p.154. Tuckwell Press.

31. Garrett, William (1997) Personal communication.
32. Cockcroft, Janet. *Op. cit.*, p. 53.
33. Glass N M. (1994) *Caithness & the War*, p. 153. North of Scotland Newspapers, Wick.
34. *John O'Groat Journal*, 22/12/1933.
35. Leask, Dr James (1997) Personal communication.
36. *John O'Groat Journal*, 27/2/1931.
37. *Medical Directory*, 1939.

Chapter 9

1. Scottish Hospitals Survey: Report on the Northern Region (1946). Department of Health for Scotland p.40. HMSO, Edinburgh.
2. Minutes, Caithness Hospitals Board of Management. 26/6/48.
3. *Ibid.*, 22/7/54.
4. *Ibid.*, 11/7/49.
5. *Ibid.*, 26/2/49.
6. *Ibid.*, 9/4/49.
7. *Ibid.*, 6/6/51.
8. *Ibid.*, 6/1/51.
9. *Ibid.*, 26/5/65.
10. *Ibid.*, 8/1/49.
11. *Ibid.*, 11/2/50.
12. *Ibid.*, 26/2/49.
13. *Ibid.*, 11/2/50.
14. *Ibid.*, 21/6/50.
15. *Ibid.*, 5/10/60.
16. *Ibid.*, 5/10/60.
17. *Ibid.*, 31/5/61.
18. *John O'Groat Journal*, 12/8/66.
19. *Ibid.*, 24/2/67.
20. *Ibid.*, 2/2/68.
21. *Ibid.*, 7/7/67.
22. *Ibid.*, 16/3/79.
23. *Ibid.*, 5/12/86.
24. *Ibid.*, 3/10/87.
25. *Ibid.*, 12/6/87.
26. Roxburgh, Stella (1997) Personal communication.
27. *John O'Groat Journal*, 25/7/86.
28. *Ibid.*, 29/6/79.
29. *Ibid.*, 11/3/1890.
30. Minutes, Caithness Hospitals Board of Management, 5/7/50.
31. *Ibid.*, 14/1/50.
32. *Ibid.*, 6/1/51.

Chapter 10

1. General Medical Services in the Highlands & Islands (1967) S.H.H.D. HMSO Edinburgh p.87.
2. *Ibid.*, p.9.
3. *Ibid.* p.25.
4. *John O'Groat Journal*, 10/2/50.
5. *Ibid.*, 29/9/50.
6. *Ibid.*, 27/8/87.
7. General Medical Services in the Highlands & Islands. *Op. cit.*, p. 89
8. Smith J A. (Ed.) (1988) *Third Statistical Account of Scotland*. Edinburgh: Scottish Academic Press.
9. *John O'Groat Journal*, 15/8/69.
10. Minutes, Board of Management of Caithness Hospitals, 26/5/65.
11. *Ibid.*, 14/9/66.
12. *John O'Groat Journal*, 26/3/71.
13. *Ibid.*, 3/2/95.
14. *Ibid.*, 27/9/68.
15. *Ibid.*, 26/7/68.
16. *Ibid.*, 21/12/79.
17. *Ibid.*, 13/2/81.
18. *Ibid.*, 19/8/67.
19. *Brit. Med. J.* (1962) i, p.1486
20. *John O'Groat Journal*, 23/10/81.
21. Burns, Ian (1997) Personal communication.

Chapter 11

1. County of Caithness, Report by Medical Officer, 1950.
2. *Ibid.*, 1956.
3. *Ibid.*, 1949.
4. *John O'Groat Journal*, 6/1/1950.
5. *Ibid.*, 1/12/1950.
6. Minutes, Board of Management of Caithness Hospitals, 6/6/1951.
7. County of Caithness; Report by Medical Officer, 1957.
8. *Ibid.*, 1971.
9. Royal Burgh of Wick, Report by Medical Officer, 1966.
10. Burgh of Thurso, Report by Medical Officer, 1966.
11. *John O'Groat Journal*, 24/3/1950.
12. *Ibid.*, 19/12/1969.
13. *Ibid.*, 10/5/1996.
14. Cathcart E P., Murray A M T. & Beveridge J B. (1940) 'An Enquiry into the Diet of Families in the Highlands & Islands of Scotland'. MRC Special Reports, No. 242.

15. *John O'Groat Journal*, 29/2/1980.
16. Heasman M A., Kemp I W., Urquhart J D. & Black R. (1987) 'Childhood leukaemia in northern Scotland' *Lancet*, 1, 266.
17. Heasman M A. et. al. (1987) 'Leukaemia in young persons in Scotland: a study of its geographical distribution & relationship to nuclear installations', *Health Bulletin*, 45/3 p. 147.
18. Urquhart J D. (1991) 'Case – control study of leukaemia & non – Hodgkins lymphoma in children in Caithness near the Dounreay nuclear installation', *Brit. med. J.*, 302 p. 687.
19. Kinlen L. (1988) 'Evidence for an infective cause of childhood leukaemia' *Lancet*, 2, 10.
20. C.O.M.A.R.E. 'Investigation of the possible increased incidence of leukaemia in young people near Dounreay nuclear establishment, Caithness, Scotland', (1988) 2nd Report. HMSO.
21. Holland W W, Detels R. & Knox G. (Eds.) (1984) *Oxford Textbook of Public Health*, vol. 1. Oxford University Press.
22. *John O'Groat Journal*, 24/4/31.
23. Birch C A. (1976) *Emergencies in Medical Practice*, p. 637. Edinburgh: Churchill-Livingstone.
24. Hutcheson, Iain (1996) *Air Ambulance*, Kea Publishing.
25. Minutes, Public Health & Welfare Committee, Caithness County Council, 14/9/1946.
26. County of Caithness, Report by Medical Officer, 1955.
27. *John O'Groat Journal*, 14/2/1976.
28. *Ibid.*, 23/1/1970.
29. *Ibid.*, 16/1/1987.
30. *Ibid.*, 2/2/1990.
31. *Ibid.*, 11/12/1987.
32. Lamont, D. (1997) Personal communication.
33. *John O'Groat Journal*, 11/12/1981.
34. *Ibid.*, 19/6/1970.
35. *Ibid.*, 25/2/1966.
36. *Ibid.*, 24/3/1972.
37. *Ibid.*, 13/2/1970.
38. *Ibid.*, 15/10/1971.
39. *Ibid.*, 9/2/1908.
40. *Ibid.*, 5/11/1971.
41. *Ibid.*, 24/9/1971.
42. *Ibid.*, 30/10/1967.
43. *Ibid.*, 1/11/1968.

Chapter 12

1. The Future of Medicine: A Series of articles. (1997) *Brit. med. J.*,vol. 313
2. Lever A M L. (1993) 'Gene Therapy for Genetic, Malignant Metabolic & Infectious Diseases', *Proc. R. Coll. Physicians Edinb*, 23 424.
3. Duncan K. (1992) 'Global warning & the risk of Lyme disease & Leptospirosis in south-east Scotland', *Proc. R. Coll. Physicians Edinb.* 22 470

Index of Names

Index of Subjects